BY
Hanna Shebar

First paperback edition 2021

Book Cover & Interior design by Ashley Santoro

ISBN

Paperback 978-1-7378977-1-2
Hardback 978-1-7378977-0-5
ebook 978-1-7378977-2-9

To my mom, Natalie.
Thank you for all your support through the years.
I could never have done it without you.

Table of Contents

I

TOO GOOD TO BE TRUE

"Amor Vincit Omnia"—Love Conquers All!

For as long as I remember, love has always been an essential part of my life. I've been searching for it like a thirsty woman searches for water in a desert.

Though I have never chosen the right man to love, I guess this extreme desire to have someone by my side didn't let me choose wisely or be patient enough to allow the right one to come along. I have always been so desperate to be loved that I idealized every guy I met, and then every time, I was left disappointed and broken inside.

When I met Richard, he seemed to be the most charming, funny, and intelligent guy I'd ever known … but this Prince Charming was on a date with another girl. I mean, he was on a date with another girl and flirting with me! Thirty minutes later, he ordered that girl an Uber and never called her again, or so he told me, anyway. Red flag right there, but in my head, it all looked SO romantic; he did this because he fell in love with me at first sight. Well, at least those were my thoughts at that exact moment.

Around us time seemed to have stopped, but we were moving fast. Three hours after our first meeting we found ourselves in one of the city's most expensive restaurants talking about love, commitment, and relationships. It was already four in the morning, but I didn't feel like going home at all—I was too excited. I knew I wouldn't sleep with him that night, but I was tempted.

In the parking lot, he kissed me for the first time, and it was the most magical moment. Have you ever heard when ladies almost fainted because of a kiss? Well, it was most certainly the case with me.

He gave me a ride back home that night, and after a good-night kiss, he said, "Call me in a morning." I just laughed and flirtatiously noted that I don't call guys first. I didn't expect the response I got—he looked at me angrily and said that if I didn't call him myself, we would never see each other again. I didn't appreciate that kind of manipulation, so I just wished him a good night and stepped out of his car.

That day at 7:00 a.m. I got a good-morning text . . . and then a hundred more. He seemed to be so obsessed with me. I won't deny that I liked it, and maybe I liked it a little too much. I felt so in control. That's how it works I guess; one always loves more than the other. I just met this guy, so I really didn't care about his feelings. I enjoyed the way he made me feel.

My theory is that every relationship is a playground, and we all are players, and whoever plays the best wins . . . and I intended to win!

We spent all day together. He took me out to Malibu for brunch. Later we had dinner and went to the movies. Whether it was because of the film we picked or the kaleidoscope of events we had experienced in twenty-four hours, we ended up sleeping on each other in the movie theater. And next morning, I woke up at his place.

Everything was like a dream coming true—beautiful penthouse, handsome guy walking around wearing nothing but a towel, breakfast waiting for me. What else can one ask for?! That weekend was truly magical. We just drove around town trying new places for lunch. He even let me play my own music in his car, even though we obviously had totally different tastes in music.

Isn't it funny how hard guys try when you are just getting to know each other? They will literally do anything for you to get some extra credit.

After fewer than seventy-two hours, he introduced me to his friends as his girlfriend. Don't get me wrong, I didn't mind at all, but it seemed so rushed, and my previous dating experiences in LA had been so different from this. I thought guys in a city of angels were total freaks. No one was looking for something real, for commitment, for feelings. The casual model of relationships is a pretty common thing around here. So, when you meet a guy who gives you a full commitment after such a short period, it looks suspicious. Just like that, I got a new boyfriend. A handsome, smart, wealthy boyfriend—my very own Mr. Perfect.

The weekend was romantic, but everything comes to its end, and the end of the romance eventually became a reality. The workweek started, and with it, the routine. I was so used to my schedule and my habits that I didn't feel like giving it all up for some guy I had just met.

Every Monday, I was going to Cecconi's with a group of my closest friends. It was a tradition of a kind. Just so you understand, Monday night at Cecconi's is the busiest time of the week. The whole town is there. To get a reservation, you have to call at least a week in advance. So, there I was with my girls, sharing a good bottle of Sauvignon Blanc and good gossip when, during the second course and after two glasses of wine, I got a phone call from him.

"Hi babe!" he said. I can't even describe how much I hate those cliché nicknames. Richard was asking me a lot of questions, but I couldn't hear a thing. I was tipsy and in a crowded restaurant, so I took it outside. "Where are you? Aren't you home?" he asked. "No, I'm with my girls at Cecconi's," I said, not knowing where he was going with his questions. "Oh, wow!" he said slowly. "Yeah, I come here every Monday," I explained. "And you didn't tell me you were going somewhere?! You could have at least asked me to join you!" I didn't know what to say. Should I really have asked him to join me? Would it be a courtesy to do so? He was pissed, and I could hear it. "OK, you know what, I don't want to talk to you right now. You are drunk and I am really upset. When you get home give me a call." And just when I thought it could not get any worse, some drunk stranger passed by yelling, "Hey, Pier! Come here!"

"Who the fuck is Pier?!" Richard shouted, "You went out on a date?! Stop lying to me!" "I have no idea who Pier is! It's just some random dude," I tried to explain, but all in vain. "Yeah, right! I know you've been seeing other people! Just stop lying about it!" "Are you insane?! I'm not lying!" I said, irritated. After less than a week of knowing me, he was already playing an Othello. At first, I wanted to explain but realizing it wouldn't do me any good, I said, "You know what, whatever . . ." and before I got a chance to finish the sentence, I heard him screaming, "Whatever?! Sure, as you wish!" Then he just hung up on me.

I was nearly in tears when I got back to the table, so obviously I had to share with the girls what had just happened, but my story was interrupted by another phone call. It was my best friend's phone and guess who was calling?! Of course, it was Richard.

Could someone be more inappropriate? After he had just yelled at me five minutes before, he was calling my friend to make sure my night was absolutely ruined. I didn't hear what he was saying to her, but I couldn't help myself and grabbed the phone from her hands. "What do you want?" I asked. "Are you still at Cecconi's?" His voice was calm. "I am. Why?" "Text me when you are done. I'll come to pick you up." "No, I don't want you here." I didn't mean it, but it just came out of my mouth. Despite my wishes, he came there and picked me up in thirty minutes. I thought there would be some talking that night. There wasn't. Instead, it was a wild night of sex. The next morning when I was getting ready for work, wearing yesterday's outfit, he told me something that I always wanted to hear from every guy I ever dated but never heard. He said I should bring some stuff to his place. That was it. To me, it was proof that we had something real, something that was going to last.

That Tuesday happened to be busy for both of us. He had a business meeting during lunch, so we decided to meet for dinner and drinks in the evening. By 7:55 p.m. I was ready and waiting for him to pick me up. After sitting on a couch all dressed up for twenty minutes, at 8:15 p.m. I decided to call him, and it went straight to a voice mail. In five minutes, I called again, but still no answer. I tried his phone two more times, and after that, I just gave up on ever reaching him. There was nothing I could do, so I changed into my PJ's, washed my makeup off, got into bed, and turned the TV on. I got ditched. For the first time in my dating history, someone ditched me. I watched a movie and passed out around 10:30 p.m.

A horrible noise coming from the front door woke me up that night. Someone was knocking non-stop. Half scared and half asleep, I got out of bed and went to open the door, and there he was, at two in the morning, on my porch . . . drunk. He fell into my living room and started hugging me. I could smell the alcohol. He had been drinking, and a lot at that. "Gosh, what are you doing here?" I asked, still shocked by his appearance. "How did you even get here? Did you take an Uber?" "Uber? I don't take Uber, babe," Richard mumbled. "Well, don't tell me you drove!" I didn't get an answer to that one. "Wait, are you serious?!" I asked, concerned how a person who couldn't stand straight could drive a car. He just smiled and hugged me. "Come on! I've been calling you! Where have you been?" I started to get angry. "I had a meeting, you know that." "Do you seriously expect me to believe you got that drunk at a business meeting? And you told me it was at lunch." "Yes … I went out with my clients," he started to explain. "OK, doesn't matter. Let's get you an Uber, and you'll go home, deal?" Richard didn't answer, but one look at him and I knew there was no way for him to even make it home. I helped Richard to take his clothes off and then put him to bed.

As do all people, I had my morning routine: wake up at 7:00 a.m., yoga from 7:30-8:30 a.m., and then breakfast and getting ready to be at work by

10:00 a.m. Obviously, my routine was messed up that particular morning. At 9:00 a.m. I woke up Richard and told him I was leaving, and he should get going too. He used the bathroom and left my place without arguing. Later that day while I was at the gym my best friend Chloe texted me saying that my boyfriend had called her. I was shocked. Why would he call my friend . . . again? What could Richard possibly need from her? When I finished my workout, I called her to get all the details. Apparently, Richard was seeking advice and had also complained to her about how I had kicked him out in the morning. I was furious. Not only had he shared our dirty laundry with the world but he had also invited my friend into my personal life. I didn't hesitate a second and dialed his number. "Hi." He sounded very cold. "Can I call you back? I'm in the middle of something." "No, you can't!" I said, irritated, "Why did you call my friend?"

"I can't talk right now, Sophie," he said to me, trying to end the call. "Well, you could when you called her! What is wrong with you?" I got so angry I almost yelled. "Oh, so now we are talking like this, huh? OK, fine! What the fuck is wrong with you? You kicked me out in the morning like some puppy!" I didn't know what to answer to that one, so I said, "Are you serious? We made plans, you ditched me, then got drunk and showed up in my place in the middle of the night, and now I'm the bad guy here?" I asked bitterly. "I can't take it from you anymore! You are being annoying!" "Me? Really?" I was on the edge. "Yes! And frankly, I think you are seeing other people and fucking around!" "God, Richard, your name really suits you—you are a real Dick!" I yelled at him. No other man in my life has managed to piss me off that much and that fast. "I just can't take any more of your lies and all this shit you keep giving me! I don't need this drama!" he yelled back and hung up. I was speechless. That night I went to bed early, trying not to think about all that craziness I had experienced in the past twenty-four hours. In less than a week I had managed to start and finish a relationship. Despite my best efforts, I couldn't stop thinking about it, and those thoughts kept me awake. Around 2:30 or 3:00 a.m. I got a text—'Where are you?'—from Richard. I decided to leave it without an answer. Two minutes later another text—'Are you in bed?'—then another one—'You went out with another guy??'

I knew it would be better to ignore him, but what I didn't know was that he was not planning on giving up and stopping. Instead, he went from texting to calling. "Babe, I am so sorry!" he said when I finally picked up. "I lost my temper . . . I am so sorry!" Honestly, I didn't know what to say to that, so I said, "That's fine, let's just talk in the morning." In the morning we did talk, and everything seemed to be back to normal. Actually, it seemed to be better than normal, and on the weekend, he took me out for lunch with his brother Kai.

Kai appeared to be charming and funny, a kind guy who treated women with respect. He was single, so I instantly decided to set him up with one of my friends, I just wasn't sure with whom.

I was with my friend Mia when Richard called asking if I wanted to go out with him and his brother, and he wondered if I would invite a cute girlfriend along to join us. It was an easy choice. I decided to bring Mia. After all, I really wanted her to meet Richard. We agreed on meeting at Kai's place around 8:00 p.m. for pre-party, but when I got home, Chloe called me. Apparently, she'd had a fight with her boyfriend and needed my moral support. I couldn't help myself and asked her to go with us; and just like that our double date turned into a group date. Chloe came over to my place and together we went to Kai's.

Both Richard and his brother were very attentive and polite with my friends, and of course, both Mia and Chloe enjoyed Kai's company. I wasn't surprised, how could someone not like him? He was perfect in everything. Though I didn't want to admit it, I kind of liked him myself and in a way that wasn't appropriate, considering he was my boyfriend's brother. Since it was three girls and only two guys in our group, the boys decided to invite some other friends. After a couple of drinks at home, we took a car and headed to Hollywood.

I was very excited, but at the bar, an unpleasant surprise was waiting for me—apparently, Richard was that type of guy who prefers female friends over guy friends. There were at least seven girls, whom he called "friends," and the second we got to our table all of them surrounded me like vultures surround their prey and started asking questions about my relationship with Richard. Meanwhile, he was at the bar talking to some guys and not paying any attention to me. After an hour at that bar, we moved to a nightclub across the street. At the club I found Kai flirting with some other girl. I was disappointed. That whole night was one big disappointment. Richard didn't spend more than five minutes with me, and when guys were trying to hit on me, he didn't even really seem to care. In fact, it was his brother who was taking care of me that night. When some drunk guy started bothering me, Kai saw it from across the club and came to my rescue—"Sorry, dude! It's my brother's girlfriend. Right, Sophie?" he said, turning to me. "Yes, that's right," I answered, smiling.

It was already 2:00 a.m., and I thought it was time to call it a night. We all went outside, and though it was already May, it was freezing. Before I got a chance to ask for it, I felt a jacket on my shoulders. I turned around, thinking it was Richard. "Thank you." I smiled, seeing Kai behind me. "No problem, doll," he said to me, and his eyes lighted up with some devilish fire. "Where do you think we should go next?" he asked, turning to the group, and then he answered his own question—"there is a club close by; they are open till 4:00 a.m." "I don't know, I'm kind of tired," I said, unsure. "Come on!" Kai whispered to me. "Just the four of us! Irina, me, you, and my brother."

"Irina? Who is that?" I was confused "Oh, that

girl right there." He pointed at a girl. It was the one he had flirted with at the club. Turned out they had known each other for a long time.

"Thanks, but I think we'll go home." I refused him politely. "OK, sure," he said and kissed me on a cheek. "Night, love. See you." I gave him his jacket back; he said good night to my girls and Richard and then left with that Irina girl.

"Home?" Richard asked me. "Yeah, but we need to make sure girls get home safe." "OK, let's get them an Uber." The car was ten minutes away and I was so cold I needed something, or better, someone to keep me warm. I leaned over and tried to hug Richard, but he immediately stepped back from me. "What are you doing?" I asked, confused, without any un-derstanding of what was going on. "Stop this! Not in front of people!" he whispered, irritated. "Are you being serious? You have been distant all evening. We barely talked. All you did was flirt with some chicks all night." "Those are my clients!" he said, raising his voice. "Yeah, right! Same ones you had a 'business meeting' with the other night, huh?" I asked him sar-castically, thinking I was witty, but Richard thought differently. "I am sick of it, Sophie! Fuck it!" he said to my face, nearly yelling, and then he just walked away, leaving me in the middle of the street at 2:30 in the morning. I was shocked by his behavior, as were my girls. We had started ordering an Uber when some car pulled over and a Mexican driver yelled "Sophie?" "That would be me," I replied, confused. "Get in the car, lady. The guy ordered it for you and asked me to get you home safe." "What was his name?" I asked, not wishing to get in a stranger's car and end up as a victim of sex trafficking. His name was Richard. I knew it before the driver even answered. I was exhausted even to think how Richard humiliated me; I was so embarrassed by myself and mad for letting a guy speak to me that way. For the next five days I didn't hear a word from him and then Chloe told me that she had gotten a text from Kai the other day and he was asking about me. The next day after that Richard called. We decided to have dinner and talk. And though we did talk—but not about what happened on the weekend—it was just a smart move to get me in bed, and it worked.

It took me some time before I realized my Mr. Perfect was a jealous and demanding type, someone who craved attention and got mad if he wasn't getting it immediately. Our whole relationship was nothing but one big fight. We had only been dating for two months at that time, but it felt like two decades. Whenever I wanted to go out, I had to tell him where and with whom I was going. I couldn't have girls' night without his permission. If I had went out without him, I would have to FaceTime to prove that there were no guys with me. And yet, when it came to him, he could go out whenever he wanted with whomever he wanted. He could leave me alone on a street at night and it would still be OK. This whole thing became unbearable and two months and three weeks after we met, I broke up with him. He never called me, never texted; things between us seemed to be over.

II

DID YOU MISS ME ENOUGH TO DRINK OR DID YOU DRINK ENOUGH TO MISS ME?

For two weeks after we broke up, I was waking up and going to bed hoping he would call me. Whenever I went out, I always picked places where I knew I could run into him. All I thought or talked about was Richard; he became my obsession. I couldn't let myself call him. After all, I was the one who ended things, but I couldn't help myself missing him like crazy, either. There I was, broken inside . . . again. I started blaming myself. Maybe it was me all along. If we had gotten a second chance, I would never fight with him again. I would tell him everything. At the end of the day, all he did, he did out of love, I thought. I had spent almost two months wanting him back, and even though I was going out with other people and some of them seemed really nice, I never gave them a real shot, because the only thing on my mind was Richard.

I knew Chloe and Kai were still texting each other from time to time, but I couldn't bring myself to ask her to check on Richard through his brother. But when we all got completely wasted on Chloe's birthday, I mustered up more courage than I should have, and I asked her to call Richard and let me talk to him. She did, but he never answered. When you're drunk, you get a million brilliant ideas in your twisted mind—mine was to call Kai. "If Richard doesn't talk to us, he will definitely talk to his brother," I said to Chloe, excited. "All we need to do is call Kai. Come on," I persuaded her, and voilà Kai, unlike his brother, picked up right away. "Hi, love! What's up?" I heard his voice when Chloe put the phone on speaker. "Hey, Kai, how have you been?" Chloe asked, giggling. "Good," he said flirtatiously. "Listen, where are you now?" "West Hollywood, you?" "Home, just chilling. My friend is coming over soon." "Can we come as well?" Chloe asked him, reading my mind. "We? Who is 'we'?" he asked, confused. "Me and Sophie." Her answer only seemed to make him even more confused, and after a short pause, he said, "Sophie? She is my brother's girlfriend; there is nothing for her in my apartment if my brother isn't here." "Oh boy, they broke up like two months ago, didn't you hear?!" "They did?" He sounded interested. "Yes, they did. Can we come over?" she asked him again. "Sure," Kai said, but he sounded unsure. "Awesome!" Chloe cried, "we'll see you in a bit."

It wasn't the smartest thing in the world to do, but who cares, we were drunk in maxi ball dresses and I knew I looked fabulous that night, so why the hell not go see the brother of my ex? I mean, there was a chance of meeting Richard, so I went for it. Chloe and I got an Uber and in fifteen minutes arrived at Kai's place. He was happy to see us and acted polite and attentive as always. After a couple more drinks I started dancing, and I danced like there was no tomorrow.

"Kai?" I said, stopping for a second, "where is your brother?!" "Huh?" He looked at me, lifting one eyebrow. "Call your brother! I need him here, now!" I demanded. "Come on, love." He smiled. I seemed to amuse him with my childish drunk behavior ."let's get you some water, OK?" He grabbed my hand and helped me to get to the coach. "How are you feeling?" he asked, handing me a glass of water. "Can you call your brother, please?" I said again, ignoring his question. Richard was everything I could think of at that moment. "Love, trust me, you don't want it." "But I do!" I tried to stand up but lost my balance and nearly fell. Luckily, he caught me. "Here you go." He put me back on the couch. "You wanna go to bed?" he asked and then turned to Chloe and added, "You girls can sleep in my room and I'll stay on a couch." Chloe helped me change into clothes Kai gave us, washed my makeup off, and got me to bed. I fell asleep the very second my head touched the pillow.

When I opened my eyes in the morning, I realized both Kai and Chloe were in bed with me. First came the shock, then denial, and then I heard Kai's voice—"Morning, love," he said to me with his eyes still closed. He looked so much like his brother and yet was so different from Richard. "How you are feeling?" he asked, turning to me, "Ohh, ashamed," I said, covering my face with my hands, "and hungover. I need water." "Nothing to be ashamed of," he said, smiling. "Come on, let's get you water."

Chloe was still asleep, so we quietly walked out of the room. In daylight, everything looked and felt so different. He got a bottle of water from the fridge and handed it to me. "Thanks," I said, sitting down on the stool. "I'm sorry about last night," I said, ashamed. "Nothing to be sorry about. I like this side of you." He looked at me, and then something I never saw coming happened—he leaned into me, and before I knew it, we were kissing. "Whaa . . . stop!" I said, pulling away. "We shouldn't . . ." "Why not?" he asked, as if he genuinely didn't understand. "You know why. I dated Richard. It's wrong . . ." I said, but before I got a chance to finish the sentence, he grabbed my waist, pulled me closer, and kissed with such passion it was impossible to resist him. There was something so mysterious about him—he was dangerous and appealing. I looked at him and I knew he was trouble. "I want to see you again," he whispered to me." I shook my head. It was wrong and I knew it. "No," I said softly, "it's wrong." He looked at me, smiling with this sneaky Cheshire cat smile. "If so, then why did you kiss me back?" It was a good question, but I had no answer to it. "I don't know," I answered honestly, "but what I do know is that it won't happen again." I didn't sound very convincing. "We'll see about that," Kai said, smiling.

After Chloe and I left his place that morning all I could think of was Kai. For the first time in two months, Richard wasn't the one on my mind, and I started asking myself, did I really miss Richard, or did I simply miss the way I felt around him?

Kai texted me that day and the next day and the day after that. We had been talking all week. Although at first, I was absolutely against any interaction with him, after a while I couldn't imagine a day without talking to Kai. I could talk to him about anything in the world. Three weeks passed, but he still hadn't made a move. Unable to wait any longer, I texted him myself, asking to meet.

And I'm glad I did—it was the best night of my life. I didn't even know I could be attracted to someone that much. Kisses, touches, moans—I've never felt anything like it before. Connection on a physical and an emotional level.

We didn't sleep till seven in the morning. My whole body hurt; I had bruises all over, I had never experienced such passion before.

"So why did you never ask me out, huh?" I asked him during breakfast the next morning.

"I let you decide," he said while frying eggs in his underwear. Kai had zero culinary talent, but he looked so sexy in the kitchen. "I figured if you liked me enough you would ask me yourself, if no . . . well then no." He smiled looking at me. Smart plan and pretty romantic.

When I was around Kai, I felt more myself than ever. I was inspired, like I could do anything, be anyone I wanted to be. Around him, I became more confident—to Kai I was always the prettiest girl in the room, and he never forgot to tell me about it. With makeup or without, in a cocktail dress or an oversized T-shirt, he always found me beautiful.

It had been two months since I started seeing Kai, and in those two months, we hadn't argued or fought even once. Maybe the reason for the success of the relationship was the absence of labels. We were not dating, we were not a boyfriend and girlfriend, no, it was more like a friendship, a friendship where friends are also having fabulous sex. But I knew that sooner or later it would come to its end, so I just enjoyed every moment while it lasted.

At the end of summer, Chloe got a text message from someone unexpected. The text was simple: 'Hi, how are you?' To our surprise, it was from Richard. By that time, I had totally forgotten about him and everything related to our relationship. Richard was texting Chloe for the next couple of days asking basic questions until one day he hit her with, 'How's everything with Sophie? Is she seeing anyone?' And after Chloe told him she wasn't aware of my affairs, Richard invited her out to dinner. I really didn't care, so I told her she was more than welcome to accept an invitation.

They picked Thursday night for dinner, the same night Kai asked me out, and while I was getting ready, Chloe called me—"You're not going to believe what your Richard just texted me," was the first thing she said. "What?" I asked, excited. "He texted asking who else would be at dinner." "What?" She confused me. "Who else?" "I don't know, I guess he thought I'd bring you." "Why do you say that?" I asked, trying to hide how much I was actually enjoying it. "Ummm, let's see," Chloe said sarcastically, "when I told him it was going to be just me and him, he simply replied 'Ohhh, OK. Bye.' So, yeah, I think he was hoping to see you." I smiled at the thought of it but chose to pretend I didn't care.

In twenty minutes, Kai picked me up and we went out for dinner. I didn't know it back then, but shortly after that night, we would slowly grow apart. First, we would stop texting each other every day, then we would meet once or twice a week, and then little by little, we would lose all communication. But that's a beauty of a summer flame—you live the dream, but when the first leaves fall, they bring you back to earth. Metaphorically speaking, of course. Everyone knows there are no seasons in LA.

While I was a love failure, my friends, on the contrary, were living the time of their lives. Both Mia and Chloe had boyfriends, and I was the only single gal around. I was ready to party, flirt, dance, and was in fact quite happy with the way things were. Richard and Kai were both abroad—Richard in Europe and Kai in Mexico—so I could be sure I wouldn't run into one of them in public. By the end of September Mia had broken up with her boyfriend and I got a new member in my "single ladies" club.

You know what they say: you get what you want when you stop wanting it. So that's exactly what happened. First Richard sent me a request on Instagram, and after three days, I finally got a text. It was two short words: 'miss you.' I didn't text that I missed him too, but I encouraged him by saying that I wouldn't mind meeting sometime for drinks.

On the weekend my squad and I went out for dinner, and we picked the same restaurant Richard took me to when we had just started seeing each other. I couldn't lie to myself any longer, so I just went with my instinct and after one glass of wine I called him. "Sophie?" He sounded surprised. "Hi . . ." I was happy to hear his voice. "How are you?" he asked. "Good, you?" "I'm good. Do you wanna meet tonight? I'm at a birthday party right now. Come over here." I wasn't ready for that, but I wanted to see him. "I am with my friends . . . Is it cool if I bring them with?" "Totally!"

My heart was jumping out of my chest, my hands were sweating, I hadn't felt so nervous and so excited for a very, very long time. In less than twenty minutes we arrived at the address Richard had given me. It was his friend's house. When our Uber pulled over, I saw a figure outside the house. First I thought it was Richard, but when I got out of the car, I realized it wasn't him, it was Max, a friend of Kai's. He had introduced us over a month ago. "Hey, Max!" I said, waving at him as we approached. "Hi . . ." He looked lost and obviously didn't recognize me. "Do you remember me?" I asked, to confirm my suspicions. "You went out with us last week?" ventured, trying really hard to remember me. "No . . ." I decided it was probably for the best he didn't know who I was and just said, "never mind." He walked us inside the house and the first person I saw was Richard, and at that moment the rest of the world just stopped existing for me—all I could hear was my own racing heartbeat. He crossed the room and came to us, first greeting Mia and Chloe and then turning his attention to me. . . There was such passion in his eyes, such desire. "Hi," he whispered intimately to me and leaned in for a hug. "Hi," I said quietly in his arms, smelling his cologne and realizing how much I had truly missed Richard. It is so easy to let go of someone when you don't see them every day, when you don't hear their laugh, don't feel their touches on your skin, but all it takes is one sight of them and all your feelings for them rush back to you.

"There you are! We were looking for you," Chloe said when I bumped into her and Mia in the kitchen. "Where did you go?" Mia asked. "Just went to talk to Richard," I said, Usually you smile from ear to ear. You dance cheek to cheek. "And?" Chloe couldn't hide her interest "We are back together!" I announced, news everyone knew was coming "You are?" Mia sounded disappointed. "Did you tell him?" "About what? What do I need to tell him?" I asked her. It was annoying she decided she had a right to criticize me, especially because I was already criticizing myself. "About Kai . . ." "Look, I know how it seems, but—" But before I finished, Chloe coughed, giving us a signal to stop talking and turn around. Max was standing right behind us, eavesdropping on everything we were saying. "I remember you now!" he exclaimed. "You were with another brother," he said with a lot of pride for himself for finally solving the mystery of our acquaintance. "No, wasn't me," I said with such confidence I almost believed my own lie. "I am positive! It was you with Kai," he continued. "Who is Kai?" I started playing dumb. "Richard's brother. I met you and Kai in the parking lot of that Chinese restaurant in Hollywood." I remembered that day perfectly, and there was no point in continuing to deny it. "Yeah, right, I remember now." It looked so theatrical, but Max was too drunk to even notice. "So, how is Kai?" I asked. "Good, traveling." "Oh, nice. When is he planning on coming back?" "He was supposed to come back to LA last week but changed plans. I'm surprised you don't know, I thought you two were a thing." I felt chills run down my back. Thank God Richard was nowhere nearby to hear that. "No, we are not a thing, just friends," I explained with a fake smile. I saw Richard coming back and my heart dropped. What if Max tells him about Kai? We are all dead then. Luckily Chloe noticed Richard as well. "Hey, Max," said, touching him on a shoulder, "could you get me another drink, please?" He smiled agreeably, took her glass, and went to fill it up for her.

All night Chloe kept Max occupied and far from me, while Richard and I hugged, kissed, and held hands. . .

At 4:00 a.m., when the party was over, Richard got us an Uber and walked outside to the car. "Text me once you get home," he said, opening a car door for me. "I will," I said and kissed him. "Good night." "Good night," he replied, smiling. I was so happy; everything was perfect—except for the judgmental comments I got from my two best friends on our way home.

III

I CAN'T REMEMBER, I CAN'T FORGET

We spent the next three days in his bedroom. No arguing, no fighting, no jealousy. He was so calm, so loving, it seemed he'd changed, and I liked this new Richard. I couldn't stop thinking about what I had done to him and what would happen if he ever found out about Kai. Everything would be over between us. I was so scared that Richard may have already learned about it, and it was killing me on the inside.

Later that week, I noticed some real changes in Richard's character. I went out with girls, and he was totally fine with that; I asked him to hang another day, and he said he was busy with work and I should do something fun with Chloe or Mia instead. He wasn't trying to control me at all, and being not used to it, I went full-on crazy, thinking Richard probably just wasn't into me anymore. I started acting the exact way he used to. I was calling him ten times a day, checking where he was and whom he was with. Sometimes he didn't answer and called me back only five or six hours later, saying he just finished work. It was driving me nuts. Was it some kind of revenge? I didn't know, but what I did know was the fact I started to become an obsessive person, and not in a fun way.

On Sunday we were invited to a birthday party. Richard was supposed to pick me up at 2:30 p.m. I got ready and was waiting for him; he seemed to be late, as usual. It was 3:00 p.m. when I started calling him to check how far from my place he was, but he didn't pick up his phone. I called six times and still no answer. Ten minutes later, I opened my IG and saw that he'd posted an Insta story of himself driving to the birthday party. He just decided to go without me and not say a word. At that moment, I felt betrayed. Who was I to him? When you care about a person, when you call them a "girlfriend," you don't do stuff like this. I felt like one of those cheap girls that men have fun with, and who never mean anything to them. Was I one of them?

I sat on the floor, opened a bottle of wine I was saving for a special occasion, and started crying. Trying to find some comfort and moral support, I called Chloe. "Hi." Her voice was shaking. She was crying as well. "What happened? You OK?" I said through my own tears. "I am picking up my stuff from Amir's place." Amir was her jackass boyfriend she'd met six weeks ago. "Why? Did you get in a fight?" I asked. "He kicked me out of his car right in the middle of nowhere," she said and started crying even harder than before. "But why? What happened?" In a matter of a moment, my problems with Richard started to look not as bad as before. "He saw this one guy texting me and got pissed, stopped the car, then told me to get the hell out. He was telling me that I am a whore, and he doesn't need someone like me as a girlfriend," she started to explain. "What a fucking asshole," I said with rage. "Go get your stuff, call an Uber, and get the hell out of there! I got wine, come to my place!" I was mad, how dare they treat us like this? What was wrong with those two? "Wait, you're supposed to be at a birthday. Why are you home? I saw Richard posting videos on IG. I thought you were with him," Chloe said, confused, and I chuckled, unable to control myself. "What? What has he done this time?" She sounded mad, ready-to-punch-someone-in-the-face mad. "He ditched me . . . " I said shortly, not willing to go into details. "Asshole!" Chloe yelled out. Being best friends means that no matter how shitty things are in your own life, you put your suffering on pause to comfort your friend, and that was exactly what we did.

While Chloe was collecting her belongings, I decided to reply to Richard's Insta story. It was a long text that looked more like an article. 'Wow! Because of a party? Stop acting crazy!' he texted me back thirty minutes later. I just couldn't control myself in those seconds. Party? Did he really think that the reaction he got was all because I was upset because I missed the party?! In my next text, I told him to never call me again. A little overdramatic, but I had learned from the best.

When Chloe got to my place, she was still crying, so we opened another bottle of wine and got drunk. Three hours later, when we were already completely wasted, Amir called Chloe and started apologizing. I have to admit, I got a bit excited myself, thinking Richard was next to call me and admit what a complete ass he was. After thirty minutes on the phone, Chloe and Amir were back on good terms. I, on the other hand, was still waiting for an apology. Suddenly my phone rang—it was an incoming call from Richard. "Yes?" I made my voice sound cold. "Did you cool down?" he asked. "What? Cool down? Are you serious, Richard?" "OK, can you chill for a second?" "I am chilled, you chill!" I said and hung up. I thought he would call me back right away, but he didn't. He didn't call or text me for the next couple of days. It was officially over.

And probably it was for the best, for the last week with Richard I'd had more ups and downs than for the last three months without him. He was so unstable. One day he calls saying how much he adores you, the next day, he's gone MIA. Being in a relationship with him was equal to living on a volcano.

It had been almost a week of drama-free life when on Thursday, after I posted an Insta story, Richard reappeared. 'You look beautiful! Let's meet and talk,' he texted me. Seriously? I left him on "read," but thirty minutes later, he texted again. 'You ignoring me?? OK!' I left it without an answer as well, and later that day, I got five missed phone calls from him. Old Richard was back, and he didn't feel like leaving me alone.

On Friday he was calling me every hour, then at 4:00 p.m. phone calls stopped, and by 6:00 p.m. I got a text; it was even bigger than the one I sent him on Sunday. The short version of it said, 'I miss you, I know you are unhappy with me, I want to change it so let's meet and talk and P.S that is the last time I'm asking you to talk.' I know now that what I needed back then was to leave that one on "read" and keep living my happy life without any male drama queens in it, but what I did was quite the opposite, I texted 'OK, let's talk.' We decided to meet Saturday morning for brunch.

That Friday night Chloe was spending with Amir, so Mia and I went out without her. We were already tipsy when I got a text from Chloe saying, 'Amir just hit me.' I was shocked. Was it some kind of mistake? I started calling her, but she didn't pick up. I got really worried. What the hell was going on?! Mia tried to call her as well, but she didn't pick up her calls either. She made us both so nervous; after all, domestic violence was no joke. "Hey! Are you OK?" was the first thing I asked when Chloe finally called me back. "No," she was crying. "Tell me what happened," I insisted. "I can't talk; I will call you back." "No, wait!" I said, but before I got a chance to ask more, she hung up on me.

"What happened?" Mia was just as worried as I was. "I have no idea," I said, "but she sounded bad." I stopped for a moment. "Do you think he . . . " I paused, deciding not to say it out loud, but Mia knew exactly what I was thinking about. "I don't know . . . " she said, "let's not jump to conclusions and just wait for when she calls us back." I agreed and honestly intended to do exactly that, but I couldn't, so I started calling her myself, and finally, she picked up. "I'm home, can you come to my place?" Chloe asked me, crying. "Yes, we'll come right now. What happened, tell me." "He slapped me," she said and started crying hysterically. "Please just come to my place, I need you right now." We got an Uber and were on our way to Chloe's place. It was just a ten-minute drive, but it felt like years. I couldn't stop worrying. In my life, I have never faced domestic violence and never met anyone who had to go through that. A man who raises his hand against women cannot call himself a man. That's what I was taught as a kid, and that's what I believed for my whole life.

Finally, we arrived at Chloe's place. I was scared of what was waiting for us there—what if she was really hurt? She opened the door, and I saw her face. Thank God there were no marks on it, only tears and running mascara, but she was shaking. While she was telling us about what happened, I got a call from Richard. I was glad he called; I needed his advice. And after I told him all that happened, he stopped whatever he was doing on a Friday night to try to help me. It won me over. "She is terrified . . . do you think we should call the cops?" I asked him straight, and when Chloe heard me, she yelled through her tears "No, don't call the cops, please don't, I don't want him to go to jail." Shocked and frustrated, I told Richard I would call him back.

"What the hell was that?" I said, furiously turning my full attention to Chloe. "What do you mean you don't want him to be in trouble?" How stupid a woman in love can be! "Yes, I don't want him to go to jail! You wouldn't send Richard to jail if something like that had happened to you!" Chloe said through her tears. The comparison made me angry. "First of all, Richard would never do anything like that, and second, I would never let anyone raise a finger to me!" "Oh, really?" Chloe screamed. "Yes, really!" "Guys, can we just stop screaming at each other?" Mia protested. "It's enough Amir slapped you already, what are you trying to do, get in a fight over it and start slapping each other?" We knew she was right, but it was already impossible to stop us. "You always judge others, but look at yourself, you think you are so perfect?! You can't even decide between two brothers, not to mention it wasn't normal to sleep with Kia when you dated Richard," Chloe said to me bitterly. "You are just jealous!" I yelled at her. Offense is the best defense, after all. "Jealous of what??" She made it sound sarcastic. "We all know you liked Kai, but I was the one who got him, so just get over it already!" I shook my head, knowing I'd won the argument. "You really think you got him? Did he mention we slept together before you two ever got together?" The minute she said it the room suddenly became very quiet, and when I finally was able to make a sound, I said, "It's a lie, I don't believe any of your words." "What?" She didn't expect that reaction. "Yes, I don't believe you! I asked him if something ever happened between the two of you and he promised me that nothing did! So just stop lying." I tried to make myself sound calm, but I was angry. "Why would I lie?" Chloe asked, and it was a pretty good point. "Sophie, stop!" Mia, who couldn't take any more of that, screamed at me. "I am not going to sit straight when Sophie calls me a liar!" Chloe explained herself. Around Mia, she would always act so innocent, as a good Catholic schoolgirl. It has always pissed me off. "Because you are a liar!" I yelled at Chloe. "You always lie, no wonder I trust Kai over you!" I had no idea what got into me. It was after four in the morning, and my brain wasn't that sharp anymore.

"OK, let's call him!" Chloe said, suddenly coming up with the idea. "Call who?" I was confused. "I'll call Kai, and you ask him yourself!" "Stop this, please!" Mia said again. "Guys, please, you are drunk. In the morning, you will regret everything you said here today!" To be honest, I was already regretting it. "Stop calling him!" I screamed at Chloe. "Unlike you, not everyone likes to be embarrassed," I said snidely. Luckily for all of us, Kai didn't pick up his phone. I couldn't take this drunk conversation any longer, so I took my jacket, put my shoes on, and without saying another word, stormed out of the apartment. I was already near the elevator when I heard steps; it was

Mia running after me. "Where are you going?" she asked. "I am tired. I came to cheer her up, but I didn't sign up for that crap." "She started crying after you left, just let's go back . . . please." Mia tried to soften me, but she knew when I decide on something, it's impossible to change my mind. "I need to go home. Sorry, I can't do it right now." I went downstairs and waited for my Uber in the lobby, wondering if Chloe was telling the truth about her and Kai and trying to understand why it bothered me so much. When I got home, Richard called me. "Just wanted to check if everything is fine," he said. "It is, thank you . . . actually do you mind if I come over?" He was surprised but pleased by the call's outcome.

Fifteen minutes later, I arrived at his home. I looked out the window of my car and realized his apartment was the exact place where I wanted to be, and Richard was the only person in the whole world I wanted to be with at that moment. I got into the elevator, and when the door opened on the 16th floor, he was right there, waiting for me. From outside I stepped right into his arms. It felt so good, so safe, and so home. "I missed you," he whispered in my ear. "I missed you too." I was tired physically and exhausted emotionally.

"How are you?" Richard asked me when we were going to bed. "Tired," I said shortly and then explained: "I got into a fight with Chloe." "What did you fight about?" I tried to make something up, but I couldn't, so I only said, "Nothing important." He didn't insist on more details. "So, what happened to her?" Richard asked. "It was a crazy night. Amir slapped her." I paused, waiting for his reaction but didn't get any. "Can you believe it?! That is horrible!" I continued. "And she doesn't want to call the police!" Chloe's words pumped up in my head. Would I do the same if it has happened to me? I couldn't help but ask, "Do you think you would ever be able to slap a woman? To slap or hit me?" "No . . . " he didn't sound very reassuring. "You don't sound too sure," I said jokingly. "It's just . . . " he paused for a moment, "if I would see you with one of my friends, I don't think I would be able to control myself." It was an honest answer, and it scared me. Friends . . . what if it was his brother? I mused. And I paused to take in Richard's apartment as I had taken in Kai's apartment. I imagined Richard becoming violent, a prospect I never thought I would have to entertain. "So, you would slap me if I made out with your friend?" I said, continuing my investigation. "Why are you asking?" Richard asked suspiciously. "Did you sleep with one of my friends?" "No," I said, nervously chuckling. "With my brother?" he asked with some weird calmness in his voice. I couldn't utter a word. How did he know? Did he know all this time? What do I do now? I had a million thoughts in my mind, but not a single word came out of my mouth. Then he broke the silence—"You did, didn't you?" I wished so much I could lie and say no, but I looked into his eyes, and I knew it was the right thing to do, so I told the truth—"I did," I said quietly, fearing what would come next. To my surprise, nothing came. He remained quiet for at least a minute, and then I finally got the courage to speak to him. "Say something, please," I whispered. "What can I say?" Richard looked at me and then added, "I can only hug you." He pulled me closer and hugged me. I didn't even notice how I fell asleep in his arms.

When I opened my eyes, he was already awake. "Good morning," he said, kissing me. He seemed to wake up in a good mood, perhaps even too good considering the piece of news I'd dropped on him a couple of hours earlier. "Good morning," I said with a nervous smile. "How did you sleep?" Richard asked. "Like a baby." I still had my weird nervous smile on. "You are a baby," he said and kissed me on the forehead. Did it mean he forgave me? I knew it was better not to ask anything until he felt like talking about it, but it seemed he wanted to pretend I had never said anything, and he had never heard anything. Ignorance and delusion were our new best friends, so I had no other choice but to play by his rules. "You hungry?" he asked, getting up from bed. "You know me, I am always hungry," I giggled. "Great! Let's get dressed and go somewhere for brunch. How does that sound?" "Like a perfect plan," I said and smiled.

IV

IT WAS ALL JUST A DREAM

Richard and I were in a good place. We were the perfect couple: no fights, no hysterics, no accusations, no suspicion. We were spending all our time together and, unexpectedly for me, I wanted to stay in and just be with him. Cook dinner and watch some silly movie on a Friday night instead of going out partying. I was in love, madly in love. I was the happiest person alive, and then one day, I got a follow request on Instagram. It was from Nate, one of Richard's friends. Richard and I were still in bed when I reached for the phone and started checking my IG. "That's my friend!" I heard Richard say. I put the phone down and turned to him. "What?" I was a bit confused. "That's my friend on your Instagram," he explained. "Why did he follow you?" "I don't know, maybe because we met and that's what people do when they know each other!" I said sarcastically and then just accepted the request. "What?? You let him follow you??" Richard suddenly said, displeased with my actions. "Yes, I did, is there a problem with that?" "There is! First, you slept with my brother, and now you switched to my friends?!" I didn't know what to say. There it was. He didn't forget, and he didn't forgive. "You are not serious, are you?" I asked, knowing the answer already. "We both know it's true," he said, getting up from bed and walking to the bathroom. "Yeah, right." I got up and started to get dressed. "What are you doing?" Richard asked, coming out of the bathroom. "What does it look like I'm doing?" I said, irritated. He didn't answer. I went to the living room, grabbed my purse, and just left without saying another word to him. I was already in the elevator when I realized I had forgotten my phone, so I had no other choice but to go back to the apartment. The door was unlocked. "I am sorry," Richard, who seemed to be waiting for me to come back, said the moment I walked in. I nodded. "Let's forget it," I suggested, and that was exactly what we did for the next couple of days, but it didn't last long before our habit of fighting took over again. We were fighting about what food to get, which movies to watch, and where to go. Literally about anything and everything, and every time he finished our fight by saying, "Yes, maybe I did something wrong, but you slept with my brother!" It was always his final argument. I realized this would last for as long as we would be together; I did something that could never be undone or forgotten, and my punishment was a constant reminder of that.

Tired of our fights, I decided to spend Wednesday night with my friend Mia. I was going to pick her up from work, and then we would go to have dinner. There was this one coworker, Daniel, who she really liked, but he didn't seem to be making a move, so I decided, as a good friend, to take action myself and invite him to join us for dinner. We went to Sugar Fish and that evening we had lots of sushi and lots of sake. I had so much fun. I felt like a real-life matchmaker. We finished dinner, walked around Beverly Hills, and then I asked Daniel to give Mia a ride home, pretending to have some errands I had to run. And he was more than happy to be of service. My job as a fairy godmother was done for the night.

I was already in bed when Richard hit me up with a text asking how my dinner was. That seemed sweet; he cared how I spent my evening. Yeah, right. In his next text, he was asking whom I was with, which can also be taken as a sweet gesture. But then I got, 'Who was that guy with you?' So I started to explain the entire story from the beginning, and then I thought, how did he even know there was a guy to begin with? Was it some kind of manipulation? So, I asked him straightforwardly. But instead of a normal answer, I got, 'You were on a date, I knew you were seeing other people! How can anyone trust you?!'

Oh boy, we were back to it again. I had neither strength nor willingness to argue or fight with him again, so I tried to call and have a normal conversation, but he simply didn't pick up his phone. That was such classic Richard. He was always, every single time, the one who started fights, and then, when I was already pissed off, he simply left me hanging there with my rage. But his all-time favorite was to turn all the facts upside down and, in the end, just blame me for everything. Classic. This time wasn't any different. The next day he didn't text or call me. First I decided to let him cool off. It usually took three to four days, but I couldn't stop thinking about him, so I decided to distract myself with something. I called Chloe to help me with shopping therapy. After a long three hours, I ended up at Alo Yoga. I didn't need another yoga outfit, but it looked so amazing on me, and I thought, when Richard sees me wearing this, he will go absolutely crazy. And then it just hit me; to make him call me, all I had to do was to post a sexy picture on IG. So, I spent $175 to get an outfit I didn't really need to get my boyfriend's attention. When I got home, I took a selfie and posted it and right away got some texts from guys I used to date before Richard. I didn't have to wait too long. Twenty minutes after I shared an Insta story Richard replied, 'Wow.' I started smiling and thought that finally our fight was over, and that maybe now he would ask me out to dinner. But before I got too carried away, I received a second text from him: 'you showed off your breasts to the world like that??!!' I was shocked. What was it? Showed off? What did I show off? I hated to be accused of something I didn't do and didn't even intend to do, so I texted him, 'What do you mean? You can't see anything!' and got, 'It's not about what you can and can't see, it's about your intentions,' and then he sent me a pic of his hard penis in shorts saying, 'will it be OK for me to post it? You can't see anything anyway!' I got pissed. What was wrong with that person? I posted that pic to get his attention and stop the fight we'd had in the first place, and he turned everything upside down once again. I really didn't want to continue fighting about stupid things. I deleted the pic and texted, 'Whatever, I deleted already!' 'Whatever???!!! OK, whatever it is!' He got it all wrong; what I meant was "Whatever. Let's stop fighting" and not "Whatever! I don't care what you think." Oh boy, those iMessage fights were driving me nuts, first of all because he was texting way faster than I ever could, plus he was always good at manipulating me. I started calling him, but he didn't answer. Who needed a boyfriend who acted like a girlfriend?! Always upset with me, always mad.

Two days later, he finally called me, asking to meet and talk. I agreed to because I also had something to say to him. I felt that all those fights needed to come to an end; I wanted to have a normal relationship, not the time bomb we had. Richard picked me up at 9:00 p.m. that evening. When I got into his car, I tried to kiss him, but he moved away, avoiding it. I knew something was wrong right away. Was he still mad? I asked but didn't get a normal answer. We were silent the entire way to his place. Finally, we got to the apartment. I wanted to break the silence but didn't know where to start, so I started all wrong. "Richard, you are not mad at me, are you?" I asked. God, could anyone have chosen a better opener? He looked at me and, after a pause, said, "I'm going to change and come right back, you need anything?" I shook my head and sat on the couch, waiting for him. What was he going to tell me? What if he wanted to break up with me? With this thought, my heart dropped, but Richard interrupted my thinking; he walked into the living room and sat on a couch next to me. "I wanted to talk," he said, taking my hand in his. "It cannot be this way anymore." "I agree, all those fights—" I hadn't finished when he interrupted, "All those fights are because you provoke me." I provoked him?! Me? I didn't say anything because if I had, we would have gotten into another fight all over again. "You have a boyfriend, but you act as if you don't, and of course, it bothers me." He continued, "What you post on your Instagram is inappropriate!" I couldn't remain silent anymore, so I opened my big mouth and started talking. "And what do I post?" I asked him, irritated. "What's wrong with my posts?" My stubborn self woke up from sleep. "You like some half-naked girls on Instagram, but I can't even post anything, right?" "OK, give me your phone. I want to see something!" He began getting angry. "What do you want with my phone?" I asked, not knowing where he was going with the demand. "I have never seen a person in a relationship post anything similar to what you post, but maybe among your friends it's normal, so let's open your Instagram feed and check together." "OK, let's." I got angry and almost threw my phone at him. While he was scrolling the feed, I started doubting myself. Maybe he was right? Now my posts started to look inappropriate even to me, but I still couldn't admit it to Richard.

"You see my point?" he asked. I couldn't fight

with him anymore, so I just said, "I won't post anything like it again." He smiled. Lord, how much I missed his smile. "Promise?" "Promise!" I smiled too. "Now, can you please kiss me!" He laughed, pulled me closer, and we kissed. At that second there was no one else in the world. He was my world.

Before Richard, I didn't even imagine falling asleep in someone's arms; it was always so hard for me to sleep next to a guy. We are the most vulnerable at night, and apparently, I never had trusted anyone enough until Richard. If before I couldn't sleep hugging someone, now I couldn't sleep without a hug.

That night I woke up at 3:00 a.m. sweating. I had a nightmare. I dreamed I had never met Richard. I opened my eyes, begging that it was just a dream. When I turned my head and saw him, that was the moment, I first realized I loved Richard. Despite everything, I loved him. That was the end of our fights. Richard was taking me out to dinner every evening, calling me in the morning, texting in the daytime, and making love to me at night. It was just the two of us, and we didn't need anyone else. I felt happy. I felt like I had found heaven on earth.

And just like that, October was almost gone. Halloween season arrived. For some unknown reason, every time I was dating someone, I always managed to break up with them right before a holiday; either on New Year's, Valentine's Day, or my birthday, I ended up alone. But this year was different! Finally,

I had a boyfriend. I guess I got a little too excited with a matching costumes idea for Halloween, but when I mentioned it to Richard—that we would be Jasmine and Aladdin for a party—he rejected it and I got frustrated. I finally had a boyfriend, but there was no use for him. He was so stubborn about it, so I just decided to let it go and choose myself a different costume. I decided to be a belly dancer, and wish I hadn't told Richard about it because when he heard of my plans, he threatened to break up with me if I dared to go to the West Hollywood Halloween parade half-naked. I mean, what option did I have except to ditch all of my brilliant ideas?

Finally, it was the day of Halloween. I convinced Richard to go to the parade, and we made plans to grab dinner with some of my friends after. I took clothes to work to change for the parade, got all excited, and then at 2:00 p.m. received a text from Richard asking not to go anywhere and just stay in. I was mad, furious, actually. First, he ruined my plans with costumes, and now he was trying to destroy the entire night. "Why would we stay home?" I asked him when he picked up my call. "I know you like to party, but can you do that for me, please?" Richard sounded very pitiful.

"Did something happen?" My anger went away when I heard his voice. "I'm really sick," Richard complained. "Sick?" I asked again, trying to make sure I'd heard him right. "Yes, I have high blood pleasure, and I didn't sleep last night because of it." I felt guilty.

"Can you please come over?" Richard asked, and I knew I couldn't say no. "I will. I'll finish work earlier and come to your place after," I promised.

I left the office by 4:00 p.m. People who live in LA know that it's the worst time to head somewhere; traffic is horrible at this time of the day, and a ten-minute ride could easily take forty minutes. So, there I was, escaping work, then suffering in traffic, just to get to Richard's place to find that he was perfectly fine. "Hi babe," he said when I walked in. "You look good," I said suspiciously. "I feel shitty though," he reassured me. I didn't say anything, but I knew manipulation when I saw it. "What do you want to get to eat?" Richard asked me, but I couldn't hide my disappointment; he made up this whole story just for the sake of not going to the parade with me. "I would go for sushi," I said. "OK," Richard said and smiled.

For the next forty-five minutes, we argued over where to order food from. When we finally agreed on something, and I started ordering for myself, he said something I never expected to hear from a guy—"How much do you eat? I have never seen a girl who eats that much. It's already ninety dollars, and it's all your food." That shocked me. I wanted to say a lot to him, but instead I only said, "I can pay for myself if it's a problem!" That little phrase became the beginning of an end. We finished dinner in silence, and then he asked, "What do you want to watch?" and I answered he could choose, but he insisted we watch what I wanted, so I picked *Bachelorette*, and

Richard didn't object. "If you don't want to watch it, we can choose something else, not a big deal," I said, noticing he wasn't into the movie. "Of course, I don't want to watch it!" Richard said, annoyed.

"OK, let's find something else." It wasn't a big deal and surely wasn't something worth fighting about, but apparently, Richard was feeling differently. "We have already watched half the movie! Good job, Sophie." He was getting angry, and I couldn't understand why. "Well, we can still change it and watch something else. What's the big deal here?" "Whatever, let's finish this one," he said, irritated, and forty-five minutes later, when we finished it, he spilled, "I can't believe we just watched this bullshit!"

Now I was the one getting annoyed. Typical Richard behavior. "OK, now you choose, and we will watch whatever you want," I said, handing him the remote. "No, you choose, but pick something we both can enjoy." It looked like he was missing our fights so much that he was trying to create one out of nothing. I opened Netflix and carefully started to search. "How do you feel about romantic comedy?" I asked. "Can you choose something normal?!" he said bitterly, and I kept looking without even saying a word. What was "normal" for him? Who knew? After ten minutes, I finally thought of something—"Comedy show! What do you think?" I asked. "Yeah, OK."

I pressed the "watch" button on the first comedy show I found. "Is this guy even funny?"

"I don't know, we'll see," I said, getting comfortable on the couch. "Oh, so you just picked one, so I would stop bothering you? Just to get rid of me, huh?" I didn't answer and just smiled, hoping he would smile too, and we would turn it into a joke, but he didn't. Instead, he stormed out, yelling something. "Hey!" I yelled, following him to the bedroom, "what's your problem? First, you asked me to skip the parade and come here because you pretended to be sick, and then you create all this drama over a movie." "Pretended?" he yelled before I finished, "are you serious?"

"The point is you are trying to turn everything upside down, as always." My voice was shrill, "Stop it! Stop acting crazy!" he yelled and walked to the balcony, leaving me so furious I was ready to murder him. Trying to calm myself down, I returned to the living room and turned the comedy show on. Twenty minutes later, Richard joined me. We sat on a couch without saying a word to each other for the next fifteen minutes, and then he stood up and went to the bedroom. A couple of minutes later, I turned the TV off and followed him. In the corridor, I bumped into him. "I'm going to bed," he said calmly. "I'll jump in the shower and come to you."

After the shower, all of my anger went away, and when I got to bed, I turned to Richard and hugged him. "I'm sorry. We OK now?" I asked. "Yes," he said tersely. The problem with Richard and me was the timing we needed to cool off after a fight. For me, it took five to ten minutes to forgive and forget, for him three business days to never. This time wasn't any different. He was still mad, and I knew he would stay mad at me for the next couple of days. I turned around, waiting for him to spoon me like he always did before falling asleep, but this time was different; instead of a hug, I got a pillow between my butt and his penis. "What are you doing?" I asked him, unable to hide my surprise. "I don't want to get excited tonight. I need to wake up early tomorrow," he said as an excuse. "Let's go to sleep." "OK, good night." I didn't know what else to say. "Night."

When I opened my eyes in the morning, Richard was already awake. "Good morning, sunshine," I said, rolling over and kissing him. "Good morning." He sounded cold, and I instantly knew he was mad. "Did you sleep well? You seem moody" "I couldn't sleep all night," Richard complained. "Oh, I'm sorry." "Don't worry, get ready, and I'll make you breakfast."

"OK." I smiled. He didn't say a word while we were in the kitchen. I figured the lack of sleep was the reason for his bad mood, so I didn't bother him. I finished my cereal, got dressed, and asked him to call the valet to get my car. He was quiet while we were waiting. I couldn't help myself and asked, "Are you still mad at me?" "I am!" he said and, after a pause asked, "what have you done to change it?!" I didn't know the answer. Was I really supposed to do something when it was literally not my fault? "Your car is ready," he said without even looking at me.

When we were at the door, I tried to kiss him goodbye, but he wouldn't let me. "You are doing this again!" I said, upset. "Why are you mad at me?" I needed an explanation, but he wouldn't satisfy me with one. "Don't be silly, I pulled away because I didn't brush my teeth," he said, and it was the biggest bullshit. "OK, bye," I said, disappointed. "Bye." Before he closed the door after me, I blushed and said something that I was absolutely not feeling at the moment. I said, "I love you!"—and what was even worse, he didn't say it back. He smiled and then said, "Go, otherwise you'll be late."

He didn't call me that day or the day after, so I decided to text him something nice, and I did, an apology text. Of course, I knew I wasn't perfect, and I wasn't afraid to admit it. But my sweet text never got an answer. I thought I would give him some space and wait until he was ready to talk. It was day five when I finally couldn't wait any longer and called him. I remember that evening as if it were yesterday. I was having dinner with Mia in this Italian place in Beverly Hills. After a glass of wine, I realized I had to talk to Richard. When I called, he picked up right away. He was probably waiting for my call, I thought to myself, and then I heard a cold "What?" It was Richard's voice, but he sounded so different I could barely recognize him. "How are you?" I asked. "I'm fine," Richard said tersely. "You didn't call me for a while. Are we not talking or something?" I tried to make it sound like a joke, but he didn't find it funny. "I didn't call because I had nothing to say to you." What was that supposed to mean? Was he breaking up with me? For a moment my heart stopped. I stood up and walked away from the table. "Hold on," I said, and my voice was shaking, "are you breaking up with me? You don't want me anymore?" "No," That second my world crashed. I felt like a million knives flew straight into my heart, and the person who threw them was the one I loved. "You are rude, disrespectful, and annoying, and I'm tired of that," he said, so heartlessly that I did my best not to cry. "So, you won't talk to me anymore?" I was unwilling to admit the truth. "Well, if you need something, of course, I will." "OK," I said and hung up, and when I did, I sat down on a street in Beverly Hills and started crying hysterically. I couldn't take a breath. It felt like there was not enough air in the whole world; I couldn't move, I couldn't think straight, all I could do was cry. And I did . . . for the next four days.

Mahatma Gandhi once said, "You must be the change you want to see in the world!" After five days of depression, I was finally ready to get over my breakup. I decided I would try to become that change I wished to see in my own little world. I would try to become a better, stronger, more confident person. A person who no one would ever be able to break again, and I meant it. Instead of eating ice cream and whining about how unfair my life was, I started a healthy diet, increased my gym visits to five times a week, lost three pounds, and began reading more books and learning more about energy and its influence on us.

One Tuesday I got an unexpected text. It was from Max, Richard and Kai's friend, whom I had happened to meet at a birthday party the other day. He was asking how I was, so I figured he knew about my breakup with Richard. Max was nice and sweet and seemed to care—he was a friend I really needed at that time. We started texting and calling each other almost every day; apparently, he was also going through a breakup, and who makes a better listener than someone with similar drama in their life?

I consider myself a hell of a lucky person to have so many truly beautiful souls in my life. I have had a chance to know Mia and Chloe, and not only to know them but to call them friends, family even. No matter what I was going through, they have always been there for me, holding my hand and walking side by side with me, even when, ten days after I ended things with Richard, my period was late. I was confused, scared, and lost, not sure if I was pregnant or not. The test seemed to be negative, but it was still pretty early for it to even be accurate. I had no idea if I should tell Richard or not. Three days later, I decided it was time to stop having anxiety attacks alone and time to share some with Richard. I got to work that morning, pulled myself together, and sent a text asking him to call me. In a couple of minutes, I got a very rude response—'You don't get to order me what to do anymore!' After that, I tried to call him, and he didn't pick up. I had no other choice but to tell him my news over text. But when he finally texted me back, I couldn't believe my own eyes. Who was this cruel person? He accused me of sleeping around and getting pregnant with his brother's kid, which made absolutely no sense, considering Kia had been out of the country for more than four months now. We texted each other a bunch of different unpleasant messages, and Richard even threatened to take it to court. By the end of the conversation, I was shaking, crying, and even more anxious than before. It took me almost an hour to stop crying. In my head, I was playing and replaying all those moments we have shared, all the sweet things he said to me—I recalled how he told me he loved kids—and refused to believe it was the same man I had just talked to. A man I loved was not capable of hatred. A little while after, I decided to text him one last time and make him ashamed of himself. I texted him, saying that as a grown man, he should know the power of words and know how much they can hurt. And surprisingly enough, it worked; he changed his behavior right away and promised to be there for me.

That day I scheduled a doctor's appointment, and little by little started to prepare myself for the possibility that I would have to be a single mom. But luckily for all parties involved, the universe decided differently. Two days after texting Richard, I woke up in the morning to discover myself covered in blood. My period had finally arrived.

That night I needed a drink, so I called Max and asked him to hang out with me. It didn't seem right to go alone with him, and I invited both Chloe and Mia to join us. At the club, I made myself forget everything, all the pain, physical and emotional, and I got drunk and high and didn't regret it for a single second. Max gave us a ride back home, and by 3:00 a.m. I was getting ready to go to bed when I heard my phone ringing. I was still really high, but I found my phone, and when I looked at the screen, I saw it was Richard. I answered only because I thought that maybe something bad happened. "How did you end up with Max?" I heard on the phone the second I picked up. "Well, hello to you, too," I said, trying to control myself and not laugh. "How did you end up with Max?" he asked again. How did he even know I was with Max? Did I post something on Instagram? I was too high to remember. I put the phone on speaker and checked. Yes, I did post a pic of Max and me. What was I thinking? "Answer me, how did you end up with him?" Richard was repeating like a broken record.

"Why do you even care?" I was amazed and couldn't hide it. "Because I care!" he yelled. "It's none of your business," I said, annoyed. Was he jealous? Or maybe his ego was hurt, or perhaps he still cared? I didn't know what to think. "Answer my question!" he yelled again. I don't know if it was the pot we smoked that night or stress, but I started laughing really hard. "Are you laughing at me?" Richard asked. "Richard, what do you want? Stop calling me!" I said through laughter. "I see you're with Max again, and you will regret it! I will make his life miserable!" That statement pissed me off, and I got really angry. "Oh yes, there is no one better than you in this!" I screamed, and in this scream was all the pain I had borne. "I warn you, you have no idea who you are dealing with, Sophie," "You're the one who has no idea, so stop calling, Richard!" I yelled and hung up.

I turned my phone to "do not disturb" and went to bed. In the morning, I had ten missed calls from Richard plus one "user-blocking-you-on-Instagram" message. How could I ever be in love with him? Was it my stupidity, or loneliness, or my daddy issues?

Later that day, I called Max to meet for lunch; during the meal, he told me a fascinating story of how Richard called him at four in the morning that night, accusing him of going on dates with his girlfriend. "Girlfriend?" This person broke up with me, then accused me of being a whore and conceiving a child with his brother, and then I magically became his girlfriend again. Maybe he was a psychopath, and I just didn't notice before?

"Did he threaten you?" I asked Max curiously after he was finished with the story. "Of course he did," he said, laughing, but it didn't seem very funny to me. "What did he say?" I asked, disturbed.

"Don't worry about it, he says a lot of things he doesn't mean."

During the next couple of weeks, I spent a

lot of time with Max. I found comfort in his friendship. Every time he called, we would talk for hours without even noticing. We went out together three to four times a week. I felt so comfortable with Max—maybe a little too comfortable. We were spending all our time together. After a little while, I started noticing that it was growing into something bigger than friendship from his side. He knew that Richard was my ex-boyfriend, he knew that I went out with his brother after our breakup, and he didn't judge—not one single time did I get a judgmental comment about my actions or even a judgmental look.

It was our regular rendezvous when Max brought up a subject I'd hoped never to discuss again. "Did Kai call you?" he asked me when we were together with Chloe on our way to a hookah place. "No, why?" I turned to Chloe, with whom I hadn't discussed Kai ever since that night we got in a fight over him. But she seemed not to care, and that gave me some relief. "Because he asked about you the last time we talked," Max explained. It was curious, Kai asking about me. I couldn't help but wonder, was he still thinking about me? Did he still like me?

That night I was not able to sleep, and after I woke up for the third time during the night, I took my phone, opened Instagram, and sent a follow request to Kai. In the morning, my request was accepted. But it didn't go any further; he didn't contact me in any way.

November passed really fast, and the city fell into Thanksgiving-preparation chaos. I heard neither from Richard nor from his brother, and I can't say I was upset about it. My life got back to normal, although I was still talking a lot about Richard with Max and every other person who was willing to listen. I had learned a lot about the person I thought I knew so well. There were too many people out there he had hurt over the years, and I felt terrible for him. As I learned, he was lonely because his own actions turned away almost everyone he had in his life. I heard stories that he was going crazy, having sex with every single girl he met. My illusions had been broken, there were too many obstacles to ever proceed. How could someone be so different from the pic you had of them in your head?

It was the night before Thanksgiving when I got a phone call from Richard again. I was visiting my family at the time, so I decided to keep that visit drama-free and declined the call. The next day I texted him, 'Happy Thanksgiving, Richard!' and was surprised when he responded, 'Happy Thanksgiving, darling! Hope everything is good with you!' and then sent me a follow request on Instagram. I was no longer persona non grata.

In the middle of December, Chloe and I planned a three-day trip to Las Vegas. It was a good idea to end 2017 on a funny, drunken note, and to just let all the worries, all the problems stay in the last year. It was the most spontaneous trip you could ever imagine. The idea struck us on Thursday night, and on Friday morning, we were on a plane to Sin City. By the time we landed, Chloe and I were already tipsy from the champagne we drank on the plane; by the time we got to our Venetian Hotel suite, we were completely wasted.

It wouldn't be a lie to say I don't remember anything from our first night in Vegas, and probably it's for the best because when I woke up in the morning, I had bruises all over my body and stamps all over my arms from every nightclub on the Strip.

Hungover, Chloe and I pulled ourselves together and went downstairs to have lunch.

"Holy shit!" was the first thing she said while we were waiting for the food, "I don't know what we were doing yesterday, but I bet we had fun." I tried to laugh, but my headache was killing me. It was a foggy day; nevertheless, our poor hungover eyes couldn't take any light, so we pulled our sunglasses down on our noses and ate onion soup in order to survive the day.

On our second night in Vegas, we decided to take things easy. By 8:00 p.m. we were dressed, and I posted a pic of our outfits on Instagram. It wasn't long before I started receiving complimentary messages, among them a sad-face emoji, the sender of which was Mr. Richard.

What did he mean, and why was he contacting me? In response, I just sent him a question mark and got the 'never mind' text. And that was exactly what I did; I wouldn't let him ruin my weekend.

When I got back to LA, Max invited me to go to an engagement party with him. He picked me up, and we drove all the way to OC. Halfway there, he mentioned there was a chance Richard might be at the party as well. I freaked out; it would be the first time I'd seen him since our breakup. But Max promised that if we got there and saw Richard, we would turn around and go home right away, so I planned to hold him to that promise.

When we got to the house, I was relieved Richard had decided not to attend. And thank God, because that night it became absolutely clear, not only to me but to everyone, that Max was in love with me. All night long he spent by my side, looking at me with eyes full of hope. Why does it always happen? Why is it impossible for a male and female to be just friends? Why does one always fall in love and get hurt by the other? Why do these friendships never last long? It didn't make it easier when Max got a little tipsy, and after a toast for the bride and groom, he yelled, "Does anyone have an extra ring? I would like to propose to someone special to me!" I knew our friendship was on the edge of ending. On our way home in a car full of people, he told me that all of my friends, including him, were going to Vegas for the Christmas weekend, and he asked me to join them. I promised I would think about it.

Chloe told me that she and Amir, her hideous boyfriend with whom she eventually got back together after that fight of theirs which had ended in violence, were going to Vegas too, and invited me to join them. It seemed that no one was staying in LA for Christmas except Richard, and I wasn't a big fan of the opportunity of seeing him during the holiday, so I was seriously considering going. Plus, Max was asking me literally every day, and he even offered to pay for my hotel room. The reason for my hesitation was a fear of losing him as a friend. Who knows what could happen in Vegas, and what would I do if something did? I valued his friendship too much to risk it that easily. But on Friday, when I realized everyone was leaving town or getting ready to leave it, I decided I should join them. After all, a lonely Christmas weekend in an empty city would be unbearable. Max booked me a room at the same hotel everyone was staying at. I'd chosen to spend only one night in Las Vegas and come back home on Christmas Eve together with Chloe and Amir. They all were driving, but I decided to take a forty-minute flight to Sin City to avoid traffic.

On Saturday morning, everyone left around 10:00 a.m., but my flight was at 2:30 p.m., so I had plenty of time. I went to the gym, did some grocery shopping, packed my one dress and tons of cosmetics in a purse, and then took an Uber and got to LAX by 1:30 p.m.

By the time I was passing TSA, I had started getting texts from my friends that they all were stuck in traffic, then Max called. "Sophie Joon, you will never guess who we just saw," he said with excitement. "Who?" I was curious. "Richard!" I couldn't believe it. "Richard?" I repeated.

"We met him at a gas station on the way to Vegas." I was going to Nevada to avoid him, only to find out that he was going there as well. "Yes, he is going to the airport to pick up this girl—" I cut him off in the middle. "Girl? What girl?" It was a particularly interesting detail. Not only would I have to face Richard, now I would have to face his new girlfriend. "I don't know. Listen, I got to go, but let me know when you land. I will come to the airport to pick you up," Max told me. "Sure! Talk to you soon." "Have a safe flight, Sophie Joon." Sophie Joon, I got this nickname from Richard once, and now he was going to the airport to pick up some girl to spend Christmas with. I wished I'd stayed home, but it was too late, the boarding had started. I had no idea back then, but that trip I would remember for the rest of my life.

VI

BYE-BYE BITCH

It's truly remarkable how we promise ourselves that next weekend we won't drink that much or won't drink at all, and then, consistently, we keep breaking our promises. On my flight back home, I swore to God and myself that I would never drink and would never again put myself in the position I had been in fifteen hours earlier.

One night of fun had caused me too many regrets and maybe even a lawsuit.

But let's start from the beginning.

The flight from LAX to Las Vegas landed in the desert of Nevada at 3:15 p.m. on Saturday, December 23, 2017. As soon as I left the plane, I called Max to pick me up, but he was still in traffic, halfway to Vegas, as was everyone else. So, I had no other option but to order an Uber. I knew from the beginning I was not supposed to be in that state. First, I got lost at the airport, and I'm not the type of person who usually gets lost. Then when I finally found an Uber pick-up spot at 4:20 p.m., it took me another twenty minutes to actually get an Uber. When at 5:00 p.m. I was passing by the Strip on the way to the hotel, I took a pic and posted it on Instagram. At 5:10 p.m. I got to the hotel and then managed to get lost in the casino, so by the time I finally found reception, it was 5:25 p.m. already. In any hotel, in order to check in, you need to pay a deposit from your card that will be returned to you after the check-out, but that time something seemed to be wrong with my card, so I had to call the bank and fix it. That took another fifteen minutes, and when I finally got a key to the room and went upstairs, it was 5:45 on the dot.

Chloe and Amir were still in traffic at the border between states. With a group of friends in his car, Max was almost in Vegas, and Richard was already at a hotel's restaurant having dinner, according to his Instagram. I took a quick shower and started to get ready; if I had to face Richard, I should at least look fabulous. When I was almost done with my make-up, I got two texts, one from Max saying that he was parking at the hotel and a second from no one else but Richard himself. He replied to my Instagram story, saying, 'You are here?' I chose to pretend it was a complete surprise to me that he was in Vegas as well, so I texted back, 'Yes, are you here too?' but he didn't answer anything to that.

In thirty minutes, I was ready, and Max called

me. "Are you ready? Because I am," I said when I picked up the phone. "I'm not ready yet. What's your room number? I'll come over now."

"Sophie Joon! You look gorgeous!" was the first thing Max told me when I opened the door of my hotel room. "Thank you!" I smiled. "So, does your room also look like a sex shop exhibition, or is it just mine?" He started laughing. "Don't look at me, it was my sister who chose this hotel!" Max said, explaining. I was joking of course, but I couldn't deny I liked the sexual subtext of the room. Red walls, black wooden floor, leather bed—it all screamed, "some shit will go down here tonight!"

"What is our plan for tonight?" I asked Max, inviting him to come in. "There is a party at our hotel, everyone's going." "Will Richard be there?" I smiled a carefree smile, but I was dying to finally see him again. "He actually texted Michael and me," Max said, looking at his phone.

Michael was a mutual friend Richard introduced me to some time ago, and since Max was really close with him and his wife Rebekah, I had gotten a chance to hang out with them a lot lately. "And what does he want?" I said, sitting next to Max on the couch. "He was asking about our plans."

"And?" I couldn't hide my curiosity. "Everyone is avoiding him. I don't think we'll see him tonight." "Thank God!" I said out loud, but I felt very disappointed. If I had known, I wouldn't have put so much makeup on. "OK, then go get ready because I want to play at the casino before we go to the party!"

While Max was deciding what to wear, Chloe finally got to the hotel, and the first thing she announced when I called her was that Richard was in Vegas. Everyone's obsession with that man, which I singlehandedly created, became annoying. We all needed to let him go and enjoy our vacation, and the first one to do so should me. Ever since Max told me that Richard was going to Vegas with a girl, I couldn't help but think and overthink. Was he over me? That thought would haunt me for the whole night.

Max was finally done showering, and after he decided which of the 200 outfits he'd brought for our two-day trip to wear and we were ready to go, our friend Michael showed up at my door. It seemed I would never leave that room. The second he walked in, the topic I was so sick of was brought up again: the name of the topic was Richard. He, without even knowing it, became the star of the day. Michael was really excited to share new details about Richards's girl with us. Apparently, she was from the East Coast and flew all the way to Vegas just to see him. So romantic, I was trying not to puke. After a twenty-minute story, Michael left.

"I officially need a drink!" I said. "Take something from the mini bar," Max told me. "Yeah, one glass of champagne for thirty dollars when we can go to the casino, have fun, and get free drinks, great idea!" I was upset and angry and was not doing a very good job hiding my frustration. "OK, let's go downstairs, and I'll get you a drink, and after, we can go to Michael's room to meet others." "Fine." All I could think of was that I needed a big drink.

We went to the casino's bar, and Max bought me champagne. One glass, and I got tipsy.

They had nothing but vodka and a full minibar in Michael and Rebekah's room. I'm not really fond of hard liquor, so I passed on the vodka, which left no other option but to empty their minibar. Red wine, champagne, white wine first from their room and then from Max's room—I emptied each and every bottle. By the time we were done it was 11:30 p.m., and being pretty well drunk, I lay down on the bed. "Are we going out tonight, or was that all we came here for?" I was a mean drunk. "Tickets to the event increased in cost," Michael said, checking something on his phone.

"How much?" Max asked him. "One hundred dollars per person," and while they were deciding if we should go or just pick another club, ticket sales stopped. I was drunk, annoyed, and frustrated. Why did I come? I wouldn't see Richard, I wouldn't go to the party, I could have just gotten drunk at home all the same. But then, out of nowhere, Max yelled, "Sophie let's go!" "Where?" I asked, lying lazily in bed and already not willing to go anywhere. "What do you mean 'where'? Downstairs to the club. We got a table!" Max said with some pride in his voice. "A table?" It came as a surprise. A minute ago we didn't have tickets; now we had a table. "Yes, he just texted me he got a table and is asking us to join." "Who? Who are you talking about, Max?" I was completely lost to what was happening in the room. "Your freaking ex-boyfriend, who else!"

"Richard?!" I didn't believe it at first. Did they have no dignity whatsoever? They had been avoiding his phone calls and texts all day, and now, when he got a table in a nightclub, they were more than happy to be his friends again. I was disgusted, but at the same time, I wanted to see Richard way too much to ditch this opportunity. I grabbed someone's drink from the table, not knowing whose it was or what was in it, and drank it in one go. "How do I look?" I asked Rebekah. "You look beautiful, don't worry," she said, smiling.

Max and I went first, and Michael, Rebekah, and the group of other people were supposed to join us a little later; Chloe and Amir were inside already. I remember my every heartbeat, every breath I took. I felt that I would faint if I took one more step. It seemed like it took one month to get downstairs; every second was like a minute, every minute like an hour. When we finally got inside, it was very crowded and very dark and almost impossible to find Richard's table. Max texted him, and Richard said he would come and get us. My whole body was shaking, and then I felt an arm around my waist. I turned around, and there he was. He kissed me on both cheeks but didn't move his hand. I was not supposed to feel anything, but I did. He looked at me with a smile. "How are you?" "OK." It was all I could force myself to say without getting emotional. He finally removed his hand from around my waist and led the way to the table.

The second we got there, Richard rushed to a girl who was dancing, whispered something into her ear, and she laughed. The girl! I had totally forgotten about her. Richard handed me a glass. "What is it?" I asked. "Vodka," he said shortly. I took the glass and started to study his new flame. She was skinnier than me, her hair looked shinier than mine, and everything about her I hated. Who knew it was going to be that hurtful? Even gossip about his new affair hurt me, but seeing it, seeing him hugging another girl, seeing him looking at her the way he used to look at me . . . Max noticed and asked me if everything was OK. I answered positively and made an excuse to run to the bathroom. How could it be OK when I felt like falling into a big dark hole? How would I go back there and face my ex-boyfriend being happy with someone else when I'm miserable and drunk? My chest felt stuffy, and my body felt like exploding. I sat on the bathroom floor and cried for a good ten minutes, and not just cried, but cried my soul out. The whole world just crashed down around me. Who would have known it would hurt so much? So much you can't breathe, so much that all you can do is sit on a dirty bathroom floor and cry. I hated everything at that moment. I hated the day I met him, the day I let him in and made myself vulnerable to be hurt by him. But he would not get the pleasure of seeing me like this because I would clean my face of tears and get back to the table and would be the most beautiful and happy girl over there. And I did. When I got back, Chloe and Amir were there too, and I felt relieved—my best friend would be by my side through this nightmare.

"You saw her?" I asked Chloe. "Who is she?" She knew exactly who I was talking about. "Richard's new girlfriend," I said with some sarcasm. "Too skinny, looks ill," spilled Chloe with disgust. That's why she was my best friend; she always knew how to make me feel better. "She is not even half as pretty as you are! Don't let that bitch ruin your night!" She hugged me, and for a moment, it all started to seem like I could go through it, but then I turned, and the most unpleasant picture was brought before my eyes—Richard was hugging this girl and laughing. I grabbed Chloe's drink from her hands, climbed on top of the couch, and started dancing. It was a wild demonstration to Richard that I was and always would be the best thing that ever happened to him. While I was dancing, I turned my head from time to time towards Richard to check and make sure he was watching my performance, but the next time I turned, he was already on a couch himself along with his new girlfriend. I didn't know what else to do, how to make him jealous when he had already turned his attention to someone new.

Then, when hope was almost lost, at a table right next to us, I noticed a guy I knew all the way from LA. He had tried to hit on me a couple of times, and I rejected him because Richard came back into my life, but now he was my salvation, so I went for it and yelled, "Shawn, hey!!!" He noticed me and smiled. "Chloe, Amir, help me out," I said, taking their hands and jumping off the couch. I walked to Shawn's table, grabbed him by the shirt, and kissed him, and he kissed me back. A minute later, when we finally stopped, I asked, "Is he looking?" "Who?" Shawn sounded very confused. "The guy over there, with a girl, is he looking?" I repeated my question. "He does and seems shocked." "Good! Kiss me again!" I commanded and kissed Shawn one more time. "Did he watch us?" "Yeah, and now he is coming here," Shawn said. I turned around and saw Richard, with eyes full of anger and hellfire. It looked like he was going to kill everyone in a blink of an eye. Well, it was his fault; he declared war when he brought that whore, and now he had gotten what he asked for.

He grabbed me by the hand and pulled me away from Shawn. "Go back to our table, Sophie!" Richard said in a commanding manner. I tried to rip my hand from his but all in vain. "You are hurting me, stop!" I yelled. "Then do me a favor and go back to the table!" "Fine, just let go of me, you psycho!" He withdrew his fingers, and I walked to his table, barely keeping my balance. That vodka had really gotten to me. I sat on a couch and saw Richard coming towards me a moment later. "What's your problem?" he asked me when he got close enough. "What is your problem? I'm having fun!" I answered and then stood up and rushed back to Shawn. I was just about to kiss him again when he stepped back from me. "Wow, wait!" "Why? Just kiss me. I need to make that guy jealous!" I said and tried to kiss him again. "If you really want something, let's go upstairs to my room, but I don't want to make anyone jealous." That phrase put me into a stupor. I didn't realize what I was doing till that second, using someone physically just to make my ex-boyfriend jealous. That was beneath me. So, without saying anything, I turned around and walked away, back to Richard's table.

There I had another drink, and to be honest, I don't really remember what went on after that. When I try to recall it, everything comes back as a flashback and nothing more. But what I do remember is quite enough to be embarrassed.

After another drink, I became wild and fearless, which I can say now for sure is not the best combination. Amir and Chloe left, but I didn't even really notice it. Max was still there, drunk as hell, and Michael and Rebekah had finally joined us. Richard was talking to his girl, and I was dancing in my desperate attempts to get his attention. I was dangerously close to Richard, and he was looking carefully at me as if he was trying to figure out what was going on in my head. I wish I had known myself. When I turned my back on him, I felt a slap that came right at my butt. Without any hesitation, I turned around, raised my hand, and slapped Richard's face. That was definitely not the reaction he expected. "Don't you ever dare to touch me!" I screamed. He couldn't make any sound but "OK." We stayed there for a minute just staring at each other, when his girlfriend jumped in front of him and broke up the scene, yelling at me, "Do you have a problem with my boyfriend?!" That brought me back to reality. Her boyfriend? He was my boyfriend before he ever became hers. He used to love me, not her, and whatever was going on between us, good or bad, it was only between us, so I stepped up to her and said, "Honey, I don't have problems with your boyfriend, but I do with my ex-boyfriend!" I said it with such a challenge in my voice that what came next wasn't a surprise—that skinny bitch tried to push me, but her tiny size zero against my powerful four had no effect. They say every action has a reaction, so my reaction was to push her back, and I did. What I didn't do is calculate the power with which I pushed her. The next second I realized she was already lying on the floor, and Richard was just staring at me without even helping his girl get up. The room was swimming around me, and I felt like blacking out any second when she stood up and was about to punch me in the face. I saw Richard in the middle between us, facing me. "Stop! Stop it, you two!" he said.

I don't remember how, but I ended up in one corner on a couch with Richard by my side, and she ended up on the other, alone. I was half asleep on the couch, totally unaware of what was happening when

I noticed a figure coming my way. It was Max, and before I even realized it, he grabbed my face and kissed me, and I kissed him back. All the thoughts in my head at that moment were about Richard and how it would hurt him, and that gave me satisfaction. I wanted him to be hurt. I wanted him to be hurt as much as I was. I remember turning my face to him after the kiss and Richard saying, "Nice!" and my answer, "Thanks!"

Then there was a blackout in my head, and the next scene was already taking place in my room. Michael helped Max and I get there and put us to bed, and I remember lying next to Max just to rest a little.

When I opened my eyes, it was morning. I turned my head and saw Max. That freaked me out, but then I looked down at myself. I had fallen asleep in my dress, and my shoes were still on, which meant nothing had happened. Max was dead asleep, and I wasn't surprised— considering how much he drank, he was lucky to be alive. I tried to stand up. My head was so hard to carry; my eyes were not obeying and trying to close on their own. I went to the bathroom to take a shower. It felt good; I was one step closer on the way to becoming a human being again. I finished in the bathroom and got back into bed. It was hard to think, hard to understand what had happened the night before. I was already in bed when this thought struck me—where is my phone?! Did I lose it? I rushed to my purse, trying to find it, but it wasn't there. I walked around the entire room, looking for it.

I was ready to give up when some vague recollection came into my still drunk head. I went to the make-up table, and it was right there, charging. Can't say I wasn't proud of myself. How responsible of me, even at my drunkest to manage to charge a cellphone to be prepared for the next day.

I returned to bed, relieved and relaxed, and was about to go back to sleep when I unlocked my phone and saw at least a dozen text messages, mostly all of them were from my mom and girls who were checking on me, but among those was one that caught my eye, a text from Richard Corbin. Questions like, why was he texting me? What did he want? ran through my head, but then the whole puzzle started to fall into place, and it became scarier and scarier to open that text. I slapped him. What was I thinking?! Why did I even do that? What got into me?! Too many questions, too few answers. I finally opened a text from him. I was too drunk to understand the context right away, so it took me rereading it four times to finally get a clue of what he wanted. The text was pretty much in his usual manner, 'You fuck everything I guess, lol.' Very original, very Richard, I should say. It didn't take long for me to get pissed, and without thinking twice, I texted right back. 'Oh, you are the one to talk, huh? BTW your new girl is a bitch, enjoy, you deserve it!' His girl, that's right, poor thing, she had just chosen the wrong time to argue with me. Better not to mess with someone whose heart is broken.

I felt sleepy but couldn't sleep, that text message wouldn't leave me in peace. What did Richard mean? Did he think I had something with Max? Oh, Max, that's right, he kissed me; he kissed me in front of Richard. How would I act around Max now? Should I pretend nothing had happened? Maybe if I follow his lead, I could save our friendship. I couldn't lose it, I couldn't lose him, perhaps it was selfish of me, but he seemed to be the only one there for me, always, with no questions asked and no judgment. I just couldn't afford to have anything stand in the way of our friendship. While those thoughts were keeping me sleepless, Max finally woke up. Last night he'd drunk twice as much as I did, so now he felt twice as bad. "Good morning," I said to him when I noticed he had opened his eyes. "Morning . . . my head hurts so bad," he said painfully. "Let's get ready, we need to check out by 11:00 a.m."

He helped me pack my things in silence, then at 11:00 a.m. sharp, I got downstairs to the reception to check out while Max was taking my stuff to his room. My flight back home wasn't until 5:00 p.m., so the rest of the day I was planning to spend with him and his sister. Originally the plan was to go out, have a nice lunch, then walk, maybe do some shopping and gambling, but in the end, all we did was get to the room, lie in bed, and just hang in there, suffering from hangovers. Although Max's sister didn't drink last night, she wasn't willing to get out of bed either, so we all just stayed in, ordered pizza, and watched movies. Then suddenly someone knocked on the door. It was Michael. The first thing he asked when he walked in was if we were still alive. "You guys were both so drunk! I was seriously worried to leave you alone," he said. "How did we even end up in the room?" Max asked, and I was happy he did because this question bothered me as well, and I didn't remember a thing. "You don't remember?" Michael asked, laughing. "Well, you two got drunk, and security came to Max and asked him to leave . . ." "What?" I laughed, "I don't remember that." "Yes, and I bet it was Richard who called security on him," continued Michael. "Why would you say that?" I asked, frustrated, "why would Richard do something like that?" "You didn't see him when you two kissed." Then he stopped, realizing by the look on my face that he had brought up a sensitive subject. "We what?" Max said, and it seemed he wasn't believing his own ears. "Kissed? You mean me and . . ." he looked at me. "Let's get back to Richard. Why did you say he asked security to kick Max out?" I interrupted, changing the subject. "Yes, it just looked like he . . . I'm sorry to say it, Sophie, but it all looked like he was trying to make you go with him. It's obvious, isn't it?" Michael said. But I had no idea what he was talking about. What could possibly be obvious to him when it was as clear as day that a guy was over me. He had literally brought another girl. "He has a girlfriend," I said with some sadness in my voice. "I don't think she wants to be his girlfriend anymore." Michael laughed again, and I felt ashamed. I'd started a fight with my ex's new girl, in the middle of a nightclub, at my ex's table in front of all our friends. The only way it could have been worse than it was already would be if she had defeated me and not vice versa.

After a picturesque story of my victory, Michael went back to his room, leaving me to deal with all the questions Max had. "I wish I remembered," he said suddenly. "What?" I was surprised. "I kissed you and don't even remember it." I was scared he would start talking about his feelings, but he didn't, and I felt that I was on safe soil, at least for the moment. "Last night was crazy. We all got drunk," I said, trying to change the subject. "I still can't believe I slapped Richard." "You did what?" Max seemed concerned. "You are joking, right?" he asked me, smiling. "I'm absolutely not. Why would I joke about it? I first slapped him and then punched his bitch." I couldn't hide my pride when I said it out loud. "Oh, God! He will sue us!" Max said, and he wasn't kidding. "What are you talking about? He would never sue me."

"Not to be overdramatic, but he would. You embarrassed him in public. He would never forgive you."

"Who cares about his forgiveness?!" I exhaled. "He can go ahead and try to sue me, and I will press charges for sexual harassment! Since when has it become appropriate in society to grab a girl by the ass?!" I said, annoyed. "He did that?" "He did!" I nodded. I totally forgot Max's sister was still in the room, but luckily for me, she had chosen to politely ignore this conversation. The rest of the day we spent watching

Frozen.

"Sophie Joon," said Max when we woke up from a nap around 3:00 p.m., "don't go back to LA, stay here for one more day!"

"I can't. I have my flight."

"I will get you a new ticket for tomorrow, or even better, you can come back home with us," he generously offered. "I really can't stay that long," I said. "Plus I have nothing to wear. I only brought one dress." "If that is the problem, then we go and buy you a dress right now, as many dresses as you want, actually." Max smiled. "I have to get back home. I promised Chloe I would spend Christmas Day with her."

"OK, then we should probably get going. I'll give you a ride to the airport."

It took me ten minutes to get ready. Max needed a little more than that. Though he was just giving me a fifteen-minute ride to the airport, he took it very seriously. While he was choosing what to wear, using his sister and me as fashion critics, my thoughts went all the way back to the time when Richard and I were together and how long it would usually take us to leave the house due to Richard's inability to decide what to wear and endless fashion shows he would give me in his apartment until the choice was made. There was something similar between Max and Richard.

All the way to the airport, we discussed Richard and his girl. Someone heard they were fighting all night after my little incident with them, and I couldn't help but wonder, what if Richard would really sue me? What would I do then? I would be embarrassed . . ."You sure you don't wanna stay longer?" Max asked when we pulled over at McCarran International Airport. "I'll see you back in a LA! Don't party too hard and try to stay alive," I said to Max while hugging him.

As soon as I got on that plane, I felt relieved to be leaving that place. I didn't want to go back to reality and think what one night could have caused me. I would think of it tomorrow. Today I would get to California, take a shower, dress up nicely, and go to Chloe's place to celebrate Christmas Eve among friends.

I promised myself never to go back to Las Vegas again. So far, nothing but crap had happened to me over there. I also promised to let Richard go and never ever contact him. But again, how often do we keep our promises??

VII

DON'T LOOK BACK, YOU ARE NOT GOING THAT WAY!

Somehow, ever since being little kids, we have been told to believe in miracles, to believe that good always beats evil, to believe that everything is possible . . . especially when it's Christmastime. But we don't stay kids forever, and as we grow older, we start to realize that in life, not everything is going to be the way we want it, not everything is possible, and definitely miracles don't happen as much as you thought, even if it's Christmas.

The day before New Year's Eve, Max, Chloe, and I went out. I needed it, just to forget about all the problems, fears, everything. But that night, Richard was the only thing I could think of. I thought I was finally ready to let go of him, and to my surprise, I didn't feel relieved. Maybe we never were meant to happen, but it didn't change the fact that we did. Was it good or bad? Didn't matter, he would always be part of my life, the part I couldn't cut out. But I could try and let him go.

My friends and I have always planned something special for every New Year's Eve celebration, but for some reason, our plans have always gotten canceled or changed. That New Year's was no exception. First, the plan was to have dinner at Culina in West Hollywood with a little group of friends and then head to a party in the hills at the house of one B-list celebrity I happened to go out with in the past. But then Mia's boss made her come to work, Max went to some secret-location party in DTLA, and everyone else managed to ditch us as well. So it was only Chloe and me. I can't say it was the worst-case scenario. We still had our dinner reservation, after all. After a couple of glasses of Veuve Clicquot, we came up with an idea to kidnap Mia from work. No one should spend New Year's Eve working and without friends by their side, so we paid the bill, got an Uber, and arrived in Beverly Hills by 11:00 p.m. The second we entered the place, I saw Mia and jumped right on her with a hug. "Surprise!" I screamed. "Oh my God! What are you guys doing here?" She really didn't expect it. "Well, if the mountain won't come to Muhammad, Muhammad must go to the mountain," I laughed. "Let's get you a table!" Mia was working as a manager in this restaurant in Beverly Hills—that was actually how we met each other in the first place. "Table would be awesome!" said Chloe. We picked the one right in the middle, the best table to spy on everyone.

It was thirty minutes until the next year. The better year, the year without drama, without toxic relationships. My two best friends by my side, a bottle of champagne on the table—perfect night, the perfect beginning of the New Year. I started receiving text messages from friends and family, and I knew there was one person I wanted to wish the happiest New Year of all. I took my phone and typed a text saying, 'Happy New Year!!! I hope 2018 will give you everything you are looking for. Wish you lots of happiness!' and pressed send. The text was meant for Richard. Of course, I wouldn't stop caring about him once the clock struck midnight, but it was a promising start.

"10, 9, 8, 7, 6, 5, 4, 3, 2 . . . 1! Happy New Year!"

"Happy New Year!" I said and laughed while hugging my girls. "Happy New Year! Woohoo," yelled Chloe. "Cheers! Cheers, girls!" we said alltogether, raising glasses of champagne.

We stayed in Beverly Hills for another thirty minutes, and when it became clear there were no more things worth staying for, we started desperately searching for other options. It was too late to go to the Hollywood Hills party that we were planning on going to in the first place. All our friends were in different locations, and my girls and I were all by ourselves. Then after minutes of brainstorming, I opened my IG and saw Richard's friend Nate. He was at the Unici Casa NYE party. I decided it was our best shot and just texted him asking if we could join their group. He answered positively, so we got an Uber and went to Culver City. I called him when we got there, and he came outside to meet us. He was very friendly and very polite. Nate walked us to his table, and it seemed like a promising start, but then one guy from the group came over to me. "Sophie! Oh my God, it's so nice to see you!" he said, confusing me. I'd never seen that person in my entire life. I tried to be polite and say something back to him, but the guy obviously noticed my confusion. "Las Vegas! We met there. You were at our table." "No, I wasn't!" I said, forgetting about my politeness. "I was at Richard's table!" "No! You were at our table!" he insisted and then waved at someone; his friend came over and was just as excited to see me as the first guy. They both insisted I was at their table that night. First, I denied it, but then I gave up. I barely remembered that night, so it was quite possible I'd met them and successfully forgot.

Nate poured us champagne, and all of us raised glasses to the New Year. I was talking to some girl when Chloe grabbed me by the shoulder. "Look!" she whispered, pointing with her head to some guy. "What am I looking at?" I asked, confused. "It's Shawn!" she continued. "Shawn who?" The name sounded familiar, but I couldn't remember who he was. "Shawn! The one from Vegas, come on!" Chloe said, irritated. "Oh, Jesus!" was all I could spill. "What the hell is he doing here? You think he saw me?" I asked Chloe, and the second I did, I noticed him waving at me and coming toward us. "Hi," he said, smiling, "Happy New Year!" I raised my glass with an awkward smile. Thank God he was just trying to be polite and wasn't expecting a conversation from me.

"Who was that?" Mia asked me the second Shawn walked away from us. "It was Shawn!" I said, looking at Chloe, who was obviously enjoying it. "The one she used in Vegas to make Richard jealous!" she laughed, explaining to Mia, "Poor guy almost got killed because of her. I wish you were there to see it." She wasn't even trying to hide her amusement. "Don't even start!" I said, irritated, and finished the glass in one go.

Even though there was some awkwardness in the beginning, champagne helped to overcome it, and twenty minutes later, my girls and I were having the time of our lives. When the clock struck 2:00 a.m., and the venue stopped serving alcohol, we got an invitation to go to an after-party at someone's house in Hollywood, and we happily accepted it. We shared an Uber with Nate and some other guy, so the car was pretty packed, and because of that, I didn't say anything to Nate when he first leaned into me and then hugged me.

When we got to the house, it was already filled with people and, unfortunately, mostly girls. I was trying to spot at least one cute guy, but there were none. What was the point in an after-party if there was no one to flirt with?! I got frustrated, placed my unhappy ass on a couch, and decided to spend the rest of a night there. Mia and Chloe, on the other hand, seemed to be having fun. While Chloe was smoking outside by the pool with two guys, Mia was sitting on a couch next to me, entertained by some guy. My prospects for the night didn't look good. And just when I thought it could not get any worse, Nate came to me and asked to talk in private. I didn't know how to say no to him, so I had no other choice but to follow him to the kitchen. "How's your night going?" he began. "It's good! Thank you for inviting us," I said. He looked at me, smiled, then took a deep breath. "Listen, Sophie, you know I like you . . ." I most certainly didn't know that and wasn't expecting, "maybe we can go out sometime?" I never knew how to reject someone in a polite way, but he seemed to be a nice guy, so I tried my best. "Well, you know I used to date your friend. I don't think it would be appropriate for me to accept your invitation." It seemed to be quite a decent excuse, but he didn't see any problem in it. "So what? We can go on a date in secret, and then if it grows into something serious, we'll tell Richard." I was speechless, and all I wanted to do was to yell at his face that the real reason I would never go out with him was because I was way out of his league. But again, he seemed to be so nice, so I overcame this desire and promised that we would talk about it when we were both sober. Then I ran the hell away from that kitchen and from him.

"Nate just asked me out" was the first thing I said when I got back to the girls. "Nate?" Chloe asked me to make sure she heard it right the first time. "Yeah," I said slowly. "And what was your answer?" Mia asked me. "What could it possibly be?" I replied, disgusted. "I mentioned Richard, and if Nate ever asks you two, you will say I'm still madly in love with my ex and not ready to move on." "That's insane! You don't have to make up a whole story just to reject the guy," Chloe objected. "I know; I just felt bad for him." "If you feel bad, why didn't you say yes and go out with him?" Mia laughed and then added, "Don't worry, we will cover for you." I smiled, nodding, and she smiled back at me.

After about an hour, Chloe left to spend the rest of the night with her boyfriend, and Mia was all over this guy she'd met a couple of hours earlier while I was just hanging by myself trying to avoid all the ugly guys that house was full of. In fact, when I'd just thought I had finally found a quiet spot where no one would bother me, some guy sat next to me and placed his arm around my shoulders. That unexpected move made me jump from the couch and rush to the middle of the room where the rest of the crowd was dancing. I thought at least there I could avoid all the unpleasant conversations and unwanted acquaintances. But my plan got ruined when that drunk douchebag followed me from the couch and started to grab my hands, trying to dance together. I felt like there was no escape . . . but then I turned and saw my salvation. He looked at me with this charming smile, and it was the moment when I went from misery to happiness in a second. My white knight in shining armor came to my rescue. His name was Timothy, but he preferred Tim. After he scared away that annoying, hand-grabbing guy, the DJ started to play slow music, and Tim invited me to dance. One song, and then another and another. We kept on dancing. Tim and I didn't say a single word, but we were smiling at each other nonstop.

For the next three hours, I didn't talk to anyone else except him. And it was so weird and yet felt right at the same time. I felt as if I were catching up with a friend I hadn't seen for a long time. I felt some invisible connection between us. We were making plans already. Where would we go on the weekend, in which hotel would we stay, in which restaurant would we eat?

They say we meet every person in life for a reason, and when I met Tim, I was sure we met to make each other very happy. The second I saw him, I knew it was a promise for something better, new, clean.

At seven in the morning, he ordered me an Uber, kissed me on the cheek, and asked me to text when I got home safe. All the way to my place, I couldn't stop smiling. That New Year's night was nothing I expected, and yet it was the best New Year's so far.

When I got home and was about to text Tim, I got a message from him asking if I was home and saying how nice it was meeting me. And then another one asking me to lunch the next day.

That night I slept like a baby with a huge smile on my face. A smile I hadn't had for a long time. It was good to have it back, and I felt it was planning on staying on my face for quite a long time. I was finally moving on, and it felt damn great!

VIII

OLD HABITS DIE HARD

They say the definition of insanity is doing the same thing over and over again, expecting different results. Well, I guess I was insane.

It'd been almost a week since I'd met Tim, and he still hadn't asked me out on a proper dinner date, so I lost any hope and just moved on with my men-free life. I have to admit, though it was great to finally be finished with my relationship with Richard, something was missing. Maybe I just became used to the routine, or maybe letting someone go is not a one-day thing. Anyway, there I was again, after all the promises I made, all the big statements I said, missing my ex and ready to run back to him at the first invitation. Guess I was a broken model, damaged beyond repair.

Richard, on the other hand, seemed to finally have moved on. He never texted me back in response to my New Year's Eve message. And I hadn't heard from him ever since, so I was sure he had no interest in me whatsoever. Until one day, I got a 'how's everything with you?' message. What unseen force was putting us back together every time we tried to move on? We started a conversation, and after a week of flirting over texts, he decided to take it out of the virtual world and into real life. He asked me to have lunch with him sometime, and without any hesitation, I agreed. All that time I had spent flirting with Richard made me forget about my friends, and they didn't appreciate being neglected, so I promised to see them on the weekend.

Friday had arrived, and Mia and I went to Tao for dinner. After two hours of dull talk and an overpriced meal, we were finally done and ready to pay the bill when Max called. "Hey Sophie, how are you?" he asked. "Good, how are you?" "I'm good, on my way to Tao to meet some friends. What are you up to?" Max said. "Oh, I'm actually at Tao, but we were just leaving . . ." I didn't really feel like seeing him that evening, but he cut me off in the middle. "No! Wait for me please, I'll be there in ten minutes. I missed you, Sophie Joon! We haven't seen each other in two weeks." I was tired and had no intention of staying, but he was almost crying, so I agreed. Less than ten minutes later, Max was at Tao. He introduced Mia and me to his friends. It was a big group, girls mostly, and every second one of them had a nose job, lip filler, and a bunch of Botox. After almost five years in LA, you automatically become a plastic surgery expert and can name whatever work was done in one look. It is funny how women in Los Angeles all look alike and all thanks to celebrities and their recommendations on the best plastic surgeons. As a result, women end up looking like clones of one another.

Mia and I had a couple of drinks with Max and his friends and were going to call it a night when the most unexpected question came up. "So, Sophie, have you talked to Richard recently?" Max asked me out of the blue. I was confused; how could he knew that we were talking again, and if he didn't know, why would he ask? "Why?" I replied suspiciously. "No matter, simple curiosity," his answer was. "By the way, have you heard?" he changed the subject. "About what?" "Richard is getting married," Max said with unhidden joy. For a second, I thought I heard it wrong. "He's what?" I asked again. "He is getting married. I'm sure you know the girl . . . you met her." "I met her?" I asked, still in shock. "Yes, in Vegas. That's the girl he was with . . . the one you nearly killed."

I was standing there in silence, just staring at Max without any understanding of what he was saying. Married. He was getting married. That didn't sound right, and I refused to believe it. And what about me? Did he never even care about me? Is it even possible? Is it possible he never did?

"It's not true!" I finally spilled out. "You are lying! He wouldn't do that!" I declared, trying to prevent myself from crying. "Why would I?" Max asked, "I'm sorry you didn't know, but it's true. They are living together." "How could they live together, when I know for a fact that Richard's friend is staying with him right now. Are you saying he would invite his friend to live with him if he had a 'bride to be' there? It's ridiculous," I said bitterly. "Well, he has two bedrooms, one is for his friend and one is for them," Max said, arguing his point. It all sounded very logical and yet didn't feel like the truth. I stayed silent for a minute or two and then came over to Mia. "He is getting married," I said shortly. "Who?" "Richard." Mia gazed at me for a moment and then laughed. "No way! You are kidding, right?" "Do I look like I am?" I asked, annoyed. "He is marrying that girl from Vegas." As I acknowledged it out loud, a tear rolled down my cheek. "Wait . . . I don't understand. How do you even know that?" Mia asked and waved at the bartender. "We'll need another round, thanks." She handed him a fifty. "Max just told me," I said, finishing my martini. "And you believe him?" Mia asked suspiciously. "Why wouldn't I? It all makes sense." "Does it? You broke up in November, and two months later, he is engaged to another girl? It doesn't sound like him." I knew she was right. The news of his engagement caught me unprepared. I even forgot to ask how long they had been engaged. "I'm gonna get to the bottom of it," I said, grabbing a new drink from the bartender and making my way through the crowd to Max. "How long they have been engaged?" I asked him straightforwardly. "I'm not sure, to be honest with you," he said. "How long? Answer my question," I asked again with a voice colder than ice. "Two years," he said. "Not possible!" I refused to believe it. "That is not possible . . . I've known him for almost a year .

. . are you saying he was engaged while he was dating me? Is that what you are saying?" I asked him almost hysterically. He looked at me with pity and only said one word, "Sorry . . ."

That night I couldn't sleep. From the moment I was alone and all the way until morning, I sat on my bed, my face covered in tears. I can't recall a time I cried harder. The realization of the fact that everything was a lie from the very beginning was worse than death. I was in a dark place, and not even a single ray of sunlight could break its way into it.

I wanted to take my phone and call Richard. But what would I tell him? Instead, I texted his friend, the one who was staying with him at that time. If anyone knew anything, it would be him. The text was simple. 'Hi, how's everything with you. Long time no see.' He answered very quickly and in an extremely pleasant and friendly manner. After a couple of texts, he started the subject I was interested in. 'Dick is missing you,' he texted. That was my chance to learn the truth. 'He does?' I texted back to him. 'Yes! He told me himself.' 'Isn't he getting married or something,' I wrote to him and immediately got back. 'LOL.' I was confused; what was that supposed to mean? But then two minutes later I got another text, 'Richard isn't getting married. He will call you soon.'

Hour after hour, I was waited for his call, or text, or anything, but it was already 7:00 p.m., and he still hadn't contacted me. I had almost lost hope when finally my phone beeped. It was a DM on Instagram. I waited a couple of minutes before opening it. 'Sophie, I have been thinking a lot about seeing you,' he started, 'but seeing you making out with a friend of mine made me think twice.' I was really confused. 'What friend? Who are you even talking about?' I texted. 'Max! in Vegas. You made out with him in front of everyone!' 'Well, I didn't make out with him.' 'LOL. You did on my fucking table in front of my face, stop lying. It was embarrassing!' I decided to ignore it and not to let my temper take over. I waited thirty minutes before I texted him a paragraph. 'I didn't make out with Max, he was drunk, and he kissed me; it wasn't mutual, just a drunk kiss, nothing more. People you have in your life, people you call friends, have no moral norms, and they don't care if it's your ex they are hitting on. And if we are talking about embarrassment, isn't it embarrassing that the same friends of yours have been ignoring you for the whole day until the very moment you got a table at a club?' I thought maybe this bitter text would have some effect on him and would allow him to see the bigger picture, but he ignored the whole context and only texted back, 'You made out with him! Stop lying!' The argument had exhausted me. I turned my phone off, changed into PJ's, and was dead asleep by 9:30 p.m. The following day, I woke up feeling tired—all that stress, tears, a sleepless night, and depression played a part. I called in sick and decided to spend the day in bed.

At noon I got a call from Max, but I didn't

pick up. I couldn't bear to talk to him after what he put me through thirty-six hours earlier. His lie was too big to forgive so easily. Half an hour later, he called me again and again, and I still was ignoring his calls. Then, he texted me, 'Why don't you answer? Do you know what Richard did to me?' It didn't sound good, considering how Richard and I ended things the night before 'What did he do?' I texted him, and a second later, he called me again. This time I picked up. "Hi, what happened?" I asked. "He came over to my house and beat me." "What?" I didn't believe what I'd heard. "Yes! He punched me in the face nearly ten times."

"No . . . why would he do that?" I asked, confused. "Because he found out you knew about his engagement from me," Max said, and there it was again: more lies. Why did he lie to me like that? Did he try to make Richard look bad or to make him the villain of my story? "Max," I said, irritated, "he isn't engaged, and you know it, please stop making things up." I was losing control already. "I am not making anything up. I'm going to the police station right now to report him." "Right, let me know when you do!" I said sarcastically and hung up.

Later I couldn't stop thinking about Richard and what if he really did punch Max in the face, and what would happen if Max filed the police report. Then, out of the blue, I got a text from Richard, 'I need your help with something,' and I immediately texted him back, 'Anything!'

But apparently, all he needed was my professional help with some marketing campaign, so the next couple of days we spent exchanging emails. But then, one evening, he called. "Hey, I was just wondering if you got me the list we were discussing," he asked me in a very formal manner. "Hi, I did, as promised," I said. "Great! Do you want to come over to drop it off? We can also go get some dinner." "Sure . . ." I said with a little hesitation. "Cool! Let me know whenever you are on your way."

In an hour, I was all dressed up and on my way to Richard's place with a folder of paperwork, which clearly was just an excuse. "Hey there," he said to me, opening the door. "Hi, how have you been?" It felt a little awkward. "Good, come on in." When I passed him, I smelled his cologne—Tom Ford, my favorite scent, it has always turned me on, and Richard knew about it. "I like your cologne." He only smiled at that.

I spent that night at Richard's eating dinner, watching movies, making jokes, and totally forgetting why I actually came there. It became absolutely clear that the work I did for him was nothing but an excuse to see me again, and I didn't mind. In the morning, I woke up with a big smile on my face. I was happy until Richard reminded me of Max. "You see, no wife," he said sarcastically. "Don't start." I sounded like a little kid. Richard laughed and kissed me on the forehead. "He pulled a fast one on you, I should say," he continued. "Who?" "Max, who else. Such a story." "OK, let's go eat, please," I said, changing the subject, unwilling to talk about Max and imaginary wives anymore.

After we finished breakfast, Richard went on again. "I still don't understand why you would believe that I had a wife," he said, chuckling, cleaning the table. "The story was pretty convincing actually," I said, annoyed. "Max said you were living together with her." "With who?" Richard was clearly amused. I hesitated for a second but then took a deep breath. "With that girl, you were with in Vegas!" I said with anger and jealousy. For a moment, there was nothing but absolute silence, but then I asked a question that had been haunting me for a while now. "Who was she anyway, huh?" He looked at me shaking his head. "No one, just an old friend from Chicago who you nearly killed." I looked down. "That comment wasn't necessary," I aid, ashamed. Richard pulled me closer. "I'm kidding, kid." Everything seemed to be in order. No wife, no fiance, only one girlfriend, and it was not the "old friend from Chicago" but me. After all the crazy things we had said to each other, after all the fights, all the slaps, all the violence (from my side anyway), we got back together . . . again. And I was more confident than ever this time would be different.

Oh, and it was! The first week of our reunion, we spent going out on dates and having fun, but the following week he stopped calling or texting me as often as usual, which was odd. I wasn't getting any attention from him. Whenever I called, he was too busy with work. Then one day, I got tired, took my phone, and texted him a very demanding message. 'Richard, I need you to help me understand what is going on between us. I need to know for myself, who am I to you? I want this to work, and I'm ready to put in all the effort, but I have to know that you are in this with me.' He didn't answer for six hours and then hit me with a text saying that he would call me later. I was waiting for his call all evening, preparing myself for all the scenarios, but the one he decided to play was not expected. Richard has always been an unpredictable man, but what he pulled that particular time was beyond everything.

I woke up at seven o'clock the next morning and opened my Instagram feed just to find out that while I had been waiting for his call, Richard had packed his stuff and left for Canada. The guy literally ran from me to another country. Without any hesitations or doubts, first I unfollowed and unfriended him on all my social media accounts, and second, I called Chloe and scheduled bar therapy with her later that day.

"He's such a moron, always has been," Chloe said, finishing her third glass of Aperol. "What have I done to deserve it? He ran all the way to Canada from me." I was so drunk I could barely pronounce words. "Forget about him! He's a loser!" she said, trying to cheer me up. "He's not a loser, and you know it!" "OK, fine. But look around, you can get any guy you want, and instead, you are wasting your time sitting here and crying over him." She was right, but it didn't make it easier. "What happened with that guy you met on New Year's? He was cute." "Tim," I exhaled. "Yeah, that one." "We texted each other a couple of times, but he never actually asked me out to dinner." "Pity. He was cute . . ." She paused and then raised her glass. "Here comes the toast: to the cute guys, and may they always ask us out!" Chloe giggled, "Great toast!" I laughed. Three more glasses and I was almost sleeping on the table. "I should ask him out," I mumbled. "Who, baby?" Chloe mumbled back at me. "Tim . . . it's never too late, right?" Without waiting for her answer, I unlocked my phone and started texting. "He's typing," I said, cheering. "Who does?" Chloe was confused and completely lost. "And it's done. We are going out on a date on Saturday night!" I said with pride. "With who, Richard?" "Richard my ass! Were you not listening?" I asked her, annoyed. "I'm going out with Tim!" "That's great! Richard is a dick . . ." she said, placing her head on the table.

The next two days, I spent texting back and forth with Tim. He seemed like a nice guy, and I was pretty excited to go out with him. On Saturday, he took me out to dinner, and then we headed to his friend's house. Everyone was so nice and friendly. There were a bunch of people and even someone I knew through Richard. After an hour we all went to a club. It was an underground party with house music. I've never been a fan of such events, but with the right company, it looked like something bearable. At the entrance to the club was a huge line of people trying to get in; among them I saw some familiar faces—they were Richard's friends. I decided to be an adult and went over to them to say hi, but to my surprise, not everyone could act mature, and to my "Hi, how are you?" I only got "Excuse me, do I know you?" So, I just turned around and went back to Tim. "You know them?" he asked me. I was not in the mood to explain that apparently, my ex-boyfriend's friends were rude and impolite people just like my ex himself; instead, I only said, "I thought I did, but I don't." Inside I met even more familiar faces. Everyone was there, even Michael and Rebekah, but at least they were nice to me. As soon as they noticed me, they first waved and then came over. "Sophie! It's so great to see you! I haven't seen you since Vegas!" Rebekah said, giving me a hug. "It is very lovely to see you guys as well. I hope all is good!" "Everything's great!" Michael said. "Oh, sorry, this is Tim," I said, noticing Michael was looking at my date. "Very nice to meet you!" he said to Rebekah and Michael. "Nice to meet you as well! We should get back to our group. Max is somewhere around. I'll let him know you are here," Michael said, smiled, then took Rebekah's hand and left, disappearing in the crowd. Max . . . I hadn't talked to him since that story about Richard and the marriage. Facing him at a party while I'm on a date didn't seem very appealing. "Wanna go to the bar and get drinks?" Tim asked, distracting me from overthinking. "Yeah, sure!" He took my hand and led the way through the crowd. At the bar, while ordering us drinks, he kissed me for the first time . . . and then for a second, and then ten more times.

We were kissing and dancing all night, and it

felt great until I saw Max. He was passing by when he noticed me. "Sophie, is it you?" He seemed disoriented. "No, it's not," I said jokingly, but apparently, he was already high. He only apologized and said, "You are not Sophie Joon! Sophie Joon is nice, and you aren't!" and after that, he simply turned around and left.

We didn't stay long at the club after that; it was almost two o'clock in the morning, and I felt sleepy and tired. Tim gave me a ride back home, kissed me good night, and somehow at that moment, I knew the best was yet to come.

IX

IT'S NOT LOVE, I'M JUST DRUNK

"Please don't leave with him! Just don't leave . . . please get in the car. I will give you a ride back to the city, but please don't leave with this guy!" It was 3:30 in the morning when Richard told me that in the parking lot of some hotel in the middle of nowhere. It was a gesture he had never done before and would never do again. I guess it was the most romantic moment in our dramatic love story.

Things with Tim were going great. It was simple. After all the time I'd spent with Richard, it was odd to have someone who didn't go crazy if I simply went out to have dinner with friends, someone who wouldn't block me on social media after a fight, someone who apologized if he lost his temper with me. Yes, it was simple, and that was the most appealing part of it.

We had been going out for a month when our mutual friend, whom I knew through Richard, invited us both to his birthday. "Will Richard be there?" was the first thing I asked Nate after receiving an invitation. "Honestly, I'm not sure," he said indecisively. "We haven't been hanging out lately. In fact, I invited him only 'cause we've known each other for so long, and it would be rude not to." "I'm just a little nervous about meeting him." I paused, waiting for Nate to cheer me up and say that Richard most likely wouldn't come, but all I got was, "It's going to be fine."

It had been almost two hours since I had opened my closet to choose a dress. The whole bedroom was a mess, clothes on the floor, bed, chair, makeup table, and on me. I had to choose a perfect outfit if there was even the slightest possibility of seeing Richard that night. I was not going to take any chances. I had to bring my A-game!

Nate was throwing a party at the casino hotel about 20 miles east from LA. Though the party was planned to start at nine, Chloe and I were invited to a pregame. Tim and I agreed to meet at the hotel later that night. He was attending another party earlier that evening. By 6:30 p.m., Chloe was at my place with an Uber. I was feeling so uncertain, so anxious, even the glass of champagne I took before leaving the apartment didn't help. "I'm nervous," I said, getting into the car. "It will be fine. I don't think he'll even be there," Chloe said optimistically.

When the car pulled up to the hotel, I saw Nate standing outside chatting with a girl. He noticed us too and waved. "There he is, our birthday boy!" I yelled, getting out of the car and walking toward him. "Happy Birthday, Nate!" Chloe said, giving him a friendly hug. "Thank you, guys! You remember my friend Julia?" He turned to the girl. I did remember her—she was a tall blonde girl with a very impressive amount of plastic surgery. Kind of hard not to remember someone like that. "Yes, it's nice seeing you again, Julia!" I said to her with fake politeness. After some minutes of the usual social pleasantries, we all went upstairs to the suite. A small group of people was already there, including Nate's older sister, boyfriend, friends, and DJ.

I don't know how or when it happened to me, but had become a really lightweight drinker over the years. The funniest part of it is that when I started my social life, at the age of seventeen, I was a pretty tough gal, but the moment I turned twenty-one, something flipped, turning me into a classy lady who only drank champagne and wine and could manage to get wasted after just a glass and a half. So, needless to say, when Nate started pouring vodka shots, I knew exactly what kind of night was ahead of me. I didn't have a single bite of food during the whole day in order to look skinnier than I was, and now if I took even one vodka shot, I could say goodbye to my classy self and hello to my drunk-ass crazy self. It was a tough choice, but I decided to be a responsible adult and politely pass.

Music, alcohol, birthday wishes—two hours

flew by fast—and it was already 9:00 p.m., and more guests started to show up. Some faces were familiar, some weren't, but I smiled at everyone and said what a pleasure it was to meet them or to see them again. Another thirty minutes passed, and the suite was filled with people. Then the door opened, and another group of guests arrived. "Sophie! Sophie!" I heard Chloe nervously calling me from across the room and rushing my way, "Sophie, it's him . . ." she whispered, sitting next to me, "it's Richard and . . ." she stopped for a second, ". . . and two girls." The smile disappeared from my face. In fact, I couldn't control my expressions anymore. My brain stopped functioning. All I could do and all I did was grab someone's shot from the table and finish it in one go. By the time Richard made it to the table where Chloe and I were sitting, I already felt the power and confidence of the alcohol spreading through me.

Richard and his friend Sam greeted Chloe first, and then Sam hugged me and kissed me on the cheek. It was Richard's turn to say hello to me. He looked at me for a second—it seemed he was trying to find the right words to say—then, after a hesitation, shook my hand and said, "Hi, Richard, nice to meet you." The only sound I could force myself to make was a confused "Huh?" He only smiled at me and turned his attention to Chloe, pretending I wasn't even there. "How have you been? Long time no see," he said. "Hm, not bad, what about yourself?" she asked him, hoping to understand the game he was trying to involve her in. "I have been good.

Working out. Lost a couple of pounds," he said with pride and looked at me, but I didn't react. While they continued their conversation, I finished another shot that conveniently happened to appear on a table right next to me. "I go to the gym four times a week," I heard him saying and followed his words with a comment, "PFFF," that just came out of my mouth uncontrollably, but Richard only looked at me for a second and pretended he didn't hear a thing. A little while later, he finally turned to me and asked something, but by that time, the vodka had already clouded my mind, and I didn't hear a single word he said, so I stood up and took a step towards him, but he nearly jumped, trying to get away from me. "She got up, oh gosh, tell her to stop, please. I feel she is going to slap me again," he said to Chloe, and by one look at her face, I knew she was just as confused as I. Everyone could feel the tension in the air, and the two girls he had brought with him knew better than to get involved. "Oh, for Christ's sake, Richard, just relax," I finally said, annoyed. He looked at me first and then grabbed a drink from the table and started sipping it.

Between all that, I had totally forgotten that I actually had a date and was supposed to meet him downstairs at the club around 10:00 p.m. I checked my phone, no text, but somehow it didn't bother me at all. I had more on my plate at that moment than Tim.

The whole group went downstairs to the club, and Chloe, I, and the biggest plastic-surgery fan in

LA County, Julia, headed straight to the bar. The bartender didn't have any wine or champagne, so I had to stick with cocktails. "Do you see him?" I asked Chloe. "Yes, he is right behind us at the other end of the bar," she said. "Is he looking?" "You bet," she giggled. "Who are you talking about?" Julia asked us with the unhidden curiosity only a woman with love for gossip could have. "My ex, the guy standing behind me, in the corner with two girls," I explained to her. "Oh God, he's been staring at you from the moment we got here. I was actually meaning to ask if you knew him." "Oh yeah, I do," I said sarcastically, sipping my mojito. "I went out with him once, like two or three years ago," Julia mentioned in a very casual manner. "You did?" I asked her to make sure I had heard her right. "Yeah, we went on a date, but he was just not the right guy for me," she explained, adding, "very conservative, very old school, church guy." Plastic surgery from head to toe, dressed like a streetwalker, no class, no quality, how did she even manage to get to go out with him? It was a big mystery to me. "Is he still looking?" I asked again, and Chloe nodded. "Maybe we should go someplace else," Julia suggested, and I couldn't have agreed more.

Another thirty minutes had passed. I was wasted, and I was on a dance floor. I lost my friends in the crowd but didn't care a bit. I was drinking cocktails, dancing, and having a good time, when suddenly someone grabbed my hand. I turned and saw Richard. "What are you doing?" I asked and pulled my hand back. "What are YOU doing?" he said, giving me a judgmental look. "Did you come here in that sexy dress to find a new boyfriend?" "Actually, I'm waiting for someone, someone who happens to be my date!" I told him with attitude and turned around to continue dancing. "Who?!" He said it so loudly and so aggressively that a couple next to us turned and gave him the eye. "It is none of your business, Richard! I asked you a question, and you run away from me, so I'm moving on with my life and highly suggest you get back to your date and do the same!" "Fair enough!" he said, annoyed, and turned around and walked away from me.

I was so mad, not only at my ex, who was causing scenes, but at the whole world and at myself because, despite everything, I couldn't help enjoying how jealous he got, and it made me think that maybe I still loved him. With that thought, I made my way back to the bar, and while I was ordering another cocktail, someone placed a hand on my waist, and I was just about to push them away, mistakenly thinking that someone was Richard, when I heard Tim saying, "Hey, love." I turned and saw him standing right behind me. "Oh, hey." I smiled and gave him a kiss. "How've you been?" he asked me. "I've been . . . good, very good." "Sophie, are you drunk already?" he asked, smiling. "Not enough." I hugged him, hiding my face in his chest. "OK, let's take you outside and get you some water, huh?" "OK," I agreed humbly. On our way to the patio, Tim met some friends and stopped for a quick chat, giving me an opportunity to escape, but the second I moved towards the patio, Richard got in my way and blocked it. "Hey, you!" I said, smiling, looking down at his glass. "What are you drinking there?" I asked and reached out for it. "OK, you're drunk, let me get you water," he said, concerned. "Water my ass!" I yelled at him. "Gimme that drink, now!" I ordered. "Sophie! Where have you been? I looked everywhere for you!" Chloe complained, coming my way. "You, missy, left me all by myself!" I told her and suddenly felt dizzy and nearly fell. Luckily Richard caught me right in time. "Careful," he said, helping me to stand up straight. "Chloe, you know you'll have to babysit this, right?" he asked her, pointing at me. Chloe only rolled her eyes and grabbed my hand. "Sophie, let's go find Tim," she said. "Who's Tim?" I heard Richard ask, and he sounded worried. Before Chloe had a chance to answer him, I did, turning to him and almost yelling that Tim was my date. "Good for you," Richard said bitterly, going back to his group. "Ass!" I said out loud.

Chloe helped me walk outside. Tim was there with some of his friends. "Love, there you are!" He pulled me closer and kissed me on the cheek. "Here's some water for you," he said and gave me a glass full of water with ice. "I don't want it; I want a drink!" I said and grabbed one from his hand. "Babe, this is plain whiskey. I think you are good!" he said, trying to get the glass back, but at the moment, no one was able to stop me. When I finished his drink, I turned my head and saw Richard. He seemed to follow me, so I decided to give him a little show. I pulled Tim closer and started kissing him with such passion it almost looked like he was a snack and I hadn't eaten in days. "Hey, hey, hey," he stopped me, "babe, what are you doing?" "What?" I asked. "I know it's your ex," he pointed at Richard with his eyes, "and I don't want to get in a fight. He looks at me like he is going to punch me in the face." "Eh, whatever." Disappointed, I pushed him away and started walking toward the bar. Richard followed me. "He's not the guy for you," he said. "Yeah? And who is? Maybe you?" I asked, chuckling. "Maybe me." He looked at me and then added, "Who's taking you back to the city?" "I have no idea. If you'll excuse me." I was trying to walk away, but he grabbed my hand. "I know, I will take you home!" he said with confidence. "Huh, is that so?" "Yes!" Richard said shortly. "If you haven't noticed, Richard, I'm here with the guy who I'm dating, and if anyone is taking me back to the city, it's him." I looked him in the eye. "You had your chance, and you wasted it on a trip to Canada." And on this note, I turned around and walked away.

I knew I shouldn't have been drinking that much, but all the drama with Richard made me anxious. "Hey, Sophie," I heard someone say and turned around. It was Sam, Richard's friend, who came with him. "You OK?" he asked, looking at me carefully. "I'm good, don't you worry." I was about to pay for my drink, but he had already given his card to a bartender. "Thanks, it wasn't necessary."

"Oh, finally!" some girl said when I walked into the ladies' room, "Chloe, I found her!" "You guys were looking for me?" I asked, confused. "Umm, duh! Like all night long, you keep disappearing," I heard Chloe yelling from behind one of the doors. "I know, it's just Richard . . ." I said, sitting down on a little chair by the sink. "What about him?" Chloe asked, coming out and washing her hands. "Just seeing him, it's hard, you know, brings back all the pain," I said and looked at her, hoping she would find the right words and say something, but she didn't. "Ready to go?" she asked, looking at her reflection in the mirror, and I nodded.

"Richard!" Chloe screamed the second she opened the door. "What are you doing?" she asked him. "What the hell?" came out of my mouth when I saw my ex spying on us by the restroom door. "You are following me to the restroom now?" "I've heard what they were saying about you there!" he shouted at my face. "I've heard you are going to go fuck now!" "Richard! Shut the fuck up!" I said and pushed him out of my way.

For the next half hour, I was by Chloe's side, but every time I happened to turn my head around, there he was, a ghost of my past feelings hunting me down, preventing me from moving on with my life. He noticed that I saw him and came over. "Again?" I asked, annoyed, but deep inside, I couldn't help but enjoy the fact that he was following me that night. Then the DJ played the song I liked, and I started to sing alone, "You just want attention! You don't want my heart!" I was yelling at Richard's face rather than singing. "You just hate the thought I'll meet someone new . . ." I carried on. "She's going crazy, I'm out," he said before walking away from me. It was impossible to stop my performance. "You've been going around to every party in LA, knowing I'll be at one . . . You just want attention, Richard; you don't want my heart!" Then suddenly, the room started to spin. "Wow, you OK?" I heard a man's voice when someone caught me from behind. "Who is it?" I asked Chloe. "Who is the guy?" "Tim," she said, and they helped me to sit down. "You wanna go home?" Tim asked, looking at me with disappointment. "Home? No, I don't want to go home, I'm fine, I'm having fun," I argued. "As you say," he said quietly.

It was already 2:00 a.m., and the party was moving back upstairs to the suite where we had started it. Outside the club, while Tim was talking to his friends and Chloe was flirting with some guy, I bumped into Richard again. "Hello, my brother's girlfriend!" he shouted. "Shhh! Are you crazy?!" I shushed him. "Oh, I'm sorry, my ex," he corrected and took a sip. How did he manage to take his drink outside? "I wish I hadn't met you! You ruined my life! You fucked me up so many times. You slept with my brother, for God's sake! Why do I still care about a whore like you?" "You are drunk!" I said, trying to ignore him. "Yes, I am," he laughed, "it's a birthday party, everyone's drunk, genius." I saw Tim coming my way. "Ready to go?" he asked, taking my hand. "Yes, babe," I said and theatrically leaned into him. "Where are you guys all going?" Richard interrupted.

"Upstairs, you should join," Tim said nicely. "Sure, I'll stop by for a minute," Richard said, looking at me. "Cool, we'll see you there," Tim told him and led me to the elevators.

When we got to the suite, it was already crowded with people. Somehow, we made our way to the table and sat alongside Nate and Julia. "Tim," I said loudly, trying to get his attention. He didn't hear me. "Tim!!" I yelled again. "Yes, love?" he asked, turning to me. "I need to go to the restroom; where is it?" "OK, you want me to take you there?" he asked. "Yes," I said to him, placing my hand around his neck. "Alright, get up, let's go." He helped me to stand up, and we walked to another room. There were even more people there, and mostly all of them were in line to use the bathroom. I couldn't really stand straight, so he helped me to sit down on the bed and started to talk to some guy in line. I hated this about him, his abnormal sociality and desire to talk to everyone and anyone. Then, out of nowhere, Richard appeared and sat next to me. "You are in line for the bathroom, huh?" he asked. "Isn't it obvious," I said, annoyed. "It was a rhetorical question," he replied and made a face. "Are you going there to have sex with this guy?" he asked me straightforwardly. "Don't assume others do what you do, Richard," I said, then stood up and walked to the bathroom, cutting off all the line. "Excuse me, but it's an emergency." Right when I was washing my hands, I heard Chloe's voice outside. "Sophie, open up!" I opened the door, and she sneaked in. "What's up?" I asked her. "You are alone?" she asked, surprised. "Of course I'm alone; who else would be here?!" "Richard just told me you were in the bathroom having sex with someone, so I . . ." I knew exactly what she wanted to say. "So you ran in here to prevent it," I said, smiling. "Something like that," she said. The one thing about her I always liked was that even drunk as hell, she has always been overprotective and cautious when it came to her friends. Someone knocked on the door, telling us to wrap it up.

We got back to the table. Tim and his friend were already there. "Everyone's going to go play poker," he said, "you want to join them?" "I want to eat," I said. "OK, should we go then?" "Good idea. Let's say goodbye and hit the road," Chloe suggested. We quickly wished everyone a good night, said birthday wishes to Nate one more time, and left. Strangely, I didn't see Richard anywhere among the crowd. "Did you see him, Richard?" I whispered to Chloe when we were in the corridor. "I saw him leaving," she said. "Alone or with girls?" "Alone." I felt relieved. When we got to the hotel's lobby, Tim's friend, who was apparently giving us a ride back to his place, went to the valet to get his car. "Let's go outside," Tim suggested.

We were waiting by the hotel's door when the car pulled over, and I heard someone calling my name, then the car door opened and I saw Richard coming out of it. It was as if some unseen force pushed me to him, and without acknowledging what I was doing, I found myself one moment with Tim and Chloe, the next walking toward Richard. "Sophie, get in the car, please," he said to me. "Richard, I'm leaving with my friends and my date." "Please, if you don't want to go to my place, that's fine; I'll take you home, but please don't leave with him." And when he said it, I saw the pain in his eyes. Apparently, I wasn't the only one suffering. "Please, I'm begging you!" he said again. "What do you want me to do? Get on my knees? I will if it helps." He sounded so desperate. My heart was screaming, 'Get in his car, just go, leave with him,' but my head was telling me something else, and for the first time, I decided to be restrained. "Good night, Richard! Please drive carefully," and with this phrase, I turned around and went back to Tim, and as I did, Richard got in his car and drove away.

X

WE CAN PLAY CAT AND MOUSE ALL NIGHT

I opened my eyes, not knowing where I was or what was going on, but as I looked at the pics, the previous night slowly started to fall into place.

After we left the hotel, Tim's friend drove to his place in Hollywood. There we had champagne, played music, danced a little, and then Tim and I started kissing and after a while just fell asleep in the guest bedroom.

As I was recreating the previous night in my mind, Tim woke up, and to my surprise, his reaction wasn't different from mine. For the first couple of seconds, he didn't seem to understand what was going on. "Good morning," I said, getting out of bed and walking towards the mirror. "Morning," he said. "I'm still drunk; we had too much last night," he said, touching his head. "Agreed," I said back, looking at myself in the mirror. My makeup was all over my face, and my hair looked like a bird's nest. "Gosh," I whispered to my reflection, desperately trying to brush my hair with my hands. "You went outside already?" Tim asked me. "No, I haven't." I was too busy in my attempt to turn myself back into a human being. Tim went to the living room, and I followed him. His friend was sitting there, drinking coffee. "Good morning," he said the second we walked in. "Hey, where did my friend go?" I asked him. "Oh, she left around six in the morning, right after you two fell asleep," he said. "Want some coffee?" He raised a pot, offering freshly made coffee. I politely refused. My biggest desire at that time was to get my stuff and go home. I spotted my phone hanging on the table and reached for it. There it was, ten text messages from Richard. I unlocked the screen and proceeded to read them. The first one was simple, 'Where are you?' then the next one was three minutes later, 'LOL,' and another one, 'You left with those guys?', 'Where are you?', 'Are you busy?' 'Call me', 'LOL', 'Are you with them right now?', 'OK, bye'. "Oh boy," I said out loud. "What is it?" Tim asked me right away, noticing the expression on my face. "Oh, nothing, just got lots of texts," I said and rushed to close my phone. "Hey, was it your ex yesterday that we saw?" he asked me. "Oh, I guess so," I said trying to avoid the subject, I said, "Listen, I'm gonna go. Can't wait to jump in the shower." I ordered myself an Uber, took my purse, and was about to say goodbye when Tim stopped me. "I'll walk you," he said. I agreed but wished he wouldn't. I wanted to be alone and allow myself to think over the previous night. Finally, my car arrived. I kissed Tim on the cheek. "I'll talk to you later," he said. I only smiled at that. "Bye," I said and waved, getting in the car.

On the way home, I tried to decide if I should call Richard or not, but after all, he was drunk, so what were the actual chances he felt the same way sober as he did drunk? It seemed he could tell me how he felt about me only when he was under the influence. After the exhausting debate with myself, I decided to let it be, giving him a chance to choose for himself. After all, if he wanted to be with me, he would make a move.

I didn't hear from Tim for the next couple of days, but it wasn't my concern. The fact that I hadn't heard from Richard ever since Nate's birthday party was upsetting me way more. Luckily it was time for my mom's visit, so at least for the next three weeks, I would be way too preoccupied to worry about them.

With Mom in town, I took some time off work to be able to enjoy her company to the fullest. Hikes, beach walks, concerts, theaters, and museums were on the schedule. Then one day, when my mom and I were at the Getty Museum, I finally heard from Richard. It was a story reply to a pic of one of Michelangelo's works, the nude sculpture of a man. It was an immature comment, 'Too small for you.' I laughed when I read it—it was so Richard, I thought to myself, and replied, 'It's art, you silly.' And although I didn't receive any dinner invitation, I was still thrilled to hear from him and felt optimistic.

The next couple of days, we were replying to each other's stories and flirting nonstop, but still, there was no invitation to meet. After almost a week, I decided to take it into my own hands and asked him out, but to my surprise, he politely declined. As confusing as Richard was, that shocked me deeply. Why did he text me for the whole week? Was it some sort of sick plan? I decided to act as if nothing had happened and to carry on with my busy schedule of entertainment. Then on Friday, I got a text message from Richard, 'Still on vacation?' I answered positively, and then he asked me about my plans for the weekend, which I assumed was a good sign. After the next couple of meaningless texts, I finally got what I wanted, 'Wanna go out with me tonight?' I was happy, but after he'd ditched me the last time, I chose to play hard to get. I asked him a lot of questions about the venue and the people he wanted to go with, but apparently, Richard was doing exactly the same thing. He asked me if I wanted to go out but didn't make any particular plans with me. We were playing cat and mouse all over again.

That evening, despite my expectations of finally seeing him again, I tried to avoid the possibility of being ditched and just went out with Mia. The plan was to make it a girls' night on the town, but after the first cocktail, it all turned back to Richard. Before I got a chance to text him, he texted me first. I received three texts from him asking about my location and the company I went out with; in return, I asked about the same thing. Then I invited him to come over to the Highlight Room, where Mia and I were hanging out that night, but he just texted, 'I'll let you know,' which usually in Richard's case meant he didn't want to go anywhere.

The next morning, he texted me wondering where I ended up and with whom I ended up. That was classic Richard, and although I wanted to see him, his behavior started to annoy me.

Another week of texting passed by, and it was already time for my mom to leave and go back home. I gave her a ride to the airport. It was a very rainy day, as if the weather felt my sorrow. At the airport, I posted a selfie with my mom and immediately got a reaction from Richard. 'Are you crying?' he commented to my Insta story. In fact I was, so I texted back a short 'Yes.' The next message I got was an invitation to come over, to which I, without any hesitations, gave a positive answer right away. After long goodbyes, hugs, kisses, tears, I finally left the airport and hit the road, on my way to Richard's. I was nervous, excited, and anxious. We hadn't seen each other since Nate's birthday.

As I walked into his building, my heart started to jump out of my chest, and when he opened the door and I saw his face, my heart dropped and stopped for a second. The world itself stopped. "Hi," I said softly, "Hi."

He made me breakfast in the morning, then I

left and didn't hear from him the whole week. I wasn't surprised or upset this time—Richard was the most unpredictable person in the entire universe, and after a year of knowing him, his behavior wasn't coming as a surprise anymore. So I just carried on with my life.

On Saturday, my friend, whom I hadn't seen in a couple of months, was in town, and he had a table at Warwick, so Chloe and I went there to have a couple of drinks and catch up. I posted some selfies, and it didn't take long before I got a story reply from Richard. It was in his typical drunk and jealous manner. He was asking where I was and whom I was with. I replied but didn't get anything in response. At 1:00 a.m. I was already home when I opened my IG and saw numerous videos of Richard partying like crazy at some girl's birthday. It made me angry and jealous. Somehow, I was always sure he didn't need anyone else but me, or maybe it was something I just wanted to believe in.

The next day he called me. "Hi," I heard when I picked up. "Hello," I answered. "Where are you?" Richard asked. "Home, where are you? Still partying?" I tried to make it sound as if I didn't care, but one could hear notes of jealousy in my voice. "No, I'm with my mom. Do you want to come over tonight and have dinner with us?" "Us?" I repeated after him. "Yeah, me and my mom." I hadn't yet met his mother, and it was so flattering that he wanted to introduce me to her. I agreed right away. "Perfect! Eight p.m.?" he asked. "Sure!" I said with some joy in my voice.

"OK, I'll get you an Uber at 7:45. Deal?" "Deal!" I answered.

His mom seemed to be a very lovely woman. At some point, I even started wondering how a decent woman like her ended up with kids who usually were not so lovely themselves. We were talking, joking, laughing, sharing memories, everything was going well, and I had a feeling she enjoyed my company just as much as I enjoyed hers, when suddenly I was asked a question I wasn't prepared to give an answer to— "Did my brother text you recently?" Richard asked out of the blue. I didn't know what to do or say. For a second, the only sound in the room was the breath of the three people who were present there. I was staring at my plate, then I turned my eyes first to Richard's mother, then to him. They both were waiting for my answer. "He hasn't." I made my voice sound calm. "Why are you asking?" "He's back in town," Richard said. "I thought you would be the first one he calls." He said it and looked at me carefully. It seemed he was trying to read what was going on in my mind at that moment. I only smiled and said, "No, he didn't text or call me, and I'm sure he won't," then continued with my meal.

After we finished dinner, Richard's mom left. "What was that about?" I blurted out the second we closed the door behind her. "What?" "Asking me about Kai in front of your mother? Did you try to embarrass me in front of her?" "I wasn't!" he said, cutting me off. "Stop it! I wasn't trying to do anything. I only asked you a question!" "I would appreciate it if in the future you wait until we are alone to ask me that kind of question," I said to him, but he only nodded.

The rest of the evening we spent watching movies and cuddling. It felt all back to normal. I started to believe maybe there was still hope, and perhaps after all we had been through in the past, we could leave it all behind and just be happy in the present. But when it comes to a relationship with Richard, you can't get your hopes up because every time you do, everything goes to shit.

In the morning, he gave me a ride to work. "I will call you later today," he said and kissed me goodbye. I was waiting for that call for five days when he posted a pic of himself on a plane. I was speechless and had no clue how to react, but instead of causing a scene, I only asked him where he was going and for how long, then wished him a safe trip, cried for fifteen minutes, and moved on.

A week later, I received a text message saying, "I'm back!"

XI

CAT'S AWAY, MICE PLAY

There is a saying that "when one door closes, another one opens." In my case, when one brother leaves, another comes back.

Kai was back in town, and as Richard predicted, he hurried to inform me about it.

'I'm back,' he texted me in DM. 'Welcome back,' I replied. 'That's not enough! You have to come in person with flowers,' he texted. Reading it, I smiled. 'Flowers, huh? What else?' I texted back. 'Hugs, and kisses and whatever you got on you!' Without acknowledging it, I started flirting with him. 'I missed you, Sophie! I have to see you.' I had already started texting him when, for a moment, I stopped to give it a second thought.

When it comes to girls, we are all private investigators, FBI agents, and Sherlock Holmes. Girls can dig up any information on a guy they need.

Around six months ago, when Kai was traveling, I (don't ask how) found out he wasn't traveling alone, so I searched and found the girl he traveled with on IG and followed her using a fake account I had specifically for this kind of shady business. Anyway, from what she was posting, it seemed clear to me how much they both were in love. Then at some point, I noticed a ring on her finger; although she didn't post anything directly saying they got engaged, it was absolutely clear they did. But now he was in LA texting me while she was alone in Europe. Did they break up, or was he just a cheating bastard?

'Yes, we should hang out,' I texted back to him after giving it one minute's thought. I couldn't know what was going on between the two of them, and it wasn't my fault if he was cheating on her, so I took the risk—after all, he was the best sex of my life. We were flirting for the next couple of days. He said as soon as his jet lag was over, we were going to meet.

It was spring, and it was time for LA Fashion Week. Chloe got two extra tickets to the show and invited me and my friend Candice, whom I knew from college but wasn't that close to anymore. She was one of those girly girls who wore lots of pink, drank pumpkin spice latte, and dreamt of going to Paris—in other words, she was pretty basic. But no one could argue, Candice was a kind soul, so I thought it was time to try and reconnect.

The funniest thing about LA, with its population of four million people—we continue to bump into the same ones over and over again. Fashion Week wasn't any different, same familiar faces again and again. We met everyone we knew in Los Angeles. I noticed some of Kai's friends and decided to go say hi. From the conversation, I learned that there was a party everyone was going to after the show, and I even got an invitation to join them.

"Hey, there is gonna be a house party after!" I said as soon as I got back to my girls. "Are we invited?" Candice asked. "We are girls, we are always invited," Chloe said, sharing her wisdom with Candice, and the three of us giggled.

With the tickets Chloe got for us, we had access to an open bar, which was a big mistake. After two glasses of champagne, we totally forgot the reason for our visit and started dancing, flirting with strangers, and texting random guys— in short, having the night of our lives

"Let's call Kai!" I said to Chloe, laughing. "Good idea! Let's go to the restroom and call from there." We rushed to the restroom without telling Candice. "We keep it between us, don't tell her, OK?" Chloe looked at me and nodded. I opened my purse, got my phone out, and dialed the number. Two rings later, I heard his voice. "Hello?" "Kai!" I yelled. "Sophie?" He sounded surprised. "Yeah! Aren't you happy to hear from me?" I asked.

"You kidding? Of course, I am! Where are you?"

"LA Fashion Week. Where are you? I need to see you!"

"I'm home, but I'm going to this house party, you should come too." "I am coming there, I got an invitation," I said with some pride in my voice. "Cool, cool. I'll see you there then. Call me when you are on your way, I'll meet you."

"Deal."

"Let's go home!" I said to Chloe as soon as I hung up the phone. "What? Why?" She was confused. "I got to take a shower and shave." She started laughing. "Jeez. Let's go."

We got back to Candice, made an excuse, then got an Uber and rushed to Chloe's place. "Shower, shower!" I yelled, running into the bathroom as soon as she opened the front door. "I'll get the drinks," she said from the kitchen. By the time I got out of the shower, she had two glasses of champagne in her hands ready. "Cheers!" she said, handing me one of them.

We turned on music, opened another bottle, and started dancing, then I heard my phone ringing in the bathroom. It was Kai. "Are you coming?" he asked when I picked up. "Only if you are," I said, flirting. "I'm on my way. Please come." "OK, we are getting an Uber." "We??" he sounded disappointed. "Oh, I forgot to tell you I'm with Chloe, sure you don't mind?" "Of course not! I'll see you guys in a bit," he said.

"Get ready, let's go," I yelled to Chloe from the bathroom. "I'm getting an Uber; get your shoes," she yelled back at me, annoyed. Fifteen minutes later, we were at the address I got from Kai's friends. It was the same house I went to a party at with Richard over seven months before.

"Let me call him, I don't want to go inside alone," I said, calling Kai's number. "We here," I said as soon as he picked up. "OK, coming."

The door opened, and I saw him. It had been almost nine months since we last saw each other, but he looked exactly the same. He kissed me on the cheek and then gave me a strong hug. "Oh, I missed you." It sounded very sincere, and I wanted to believe it was true. We walked upstairs. There in the big room were around twenty people, and I knew almost every one of them. Among the crowd, I noticed Max. We hadn't talked ever since that story with Richard, and it felt awkward. But he wasn't the only unpleasant surprise at the party: some of Richard's friends were there. They knew me as Richard's girlfriend, and now I was with Kai, and for some reason, I felt something I'd never experienced before—unwillingly, I judged myself.

Half an hour later, Chloe and I were sitting on the couch sipping our drinks when Max approached us. "Sophie, hi," he said, sitting down next to me. "Hi," I said with an unnatural grin. "I missed you! You have been ignoring me for months," he said and then started to explain to me something about that story with Richard, but I cut him off in the middle. "Listen, Max, I don't want to hear it, alright?" I got up and went to Kai. "This party sucks," I said to Kai, placing my head on his shoulder. He only laughed, then took a glass from my hand and took a sip. "We're gonna leave soon, wanna go to my place?" he asked, giving me my drink back. I smiled and nodded.

For another hour, I was hung out with Chloe, Kai, and some of his guy friends, when Chloe said she wanted to smoke. The three of us went to the patio. There were exactly three seats available; Kai sat next to me and was about to start a conversation when some girl interrupted us. She looked at me with hatred. I was sure I'd seen her before, she looked familiar, but I couldn't remember where I knew her from, so I leaned into Chloe. "Do you know her?" I whispered. "Richard's friend," she said quickly. "Crap!" uncontrollably came out of my mouth, and so loud both Kai and the girl could hear me. "Hey, so Linda tells me you've been here before," Kai said, turning to me. Linda, that was her name, I remembered her now, and before I got a chance to answer, that bitch Linda did it for me. "Yes! Yes, she was! With Richard," she said bitterly. I felt humiliated. Kai only looked at me and changed the subject.

"What a bitch!" I said to Chloe on our way back inside. "Can you believe it?" But she wasn't even listening to me. Chloe seemed off that evening, and I didn't know why. "Hey, I think I'm gonna go home," she finally said. "No!" I objected. "Please, we are going to Kai's place soon. You have to go with me!" I was trying to convince her to stay, "It's 4:00 a.m., and I'm tired. I'll get an Uber." "OK," I exhaled in disappointment.

A couple of minutes later, her car was outside, and I went to walk her, and Kai saw us heading to the front door. "Hey, where are you going?" he asked, grabbing my hand. "Leaving, it's late," Chloe said. "Are you leaving, too?" he asked, turning to me. "Hmm, no, I'll stay," I smiled. "Good."

Back in the house, I asked a question that was bothering me for the whole evening. "Why are you still friends with Max?" Kai stopped on the stairs and looked at me carefully. "Where is this coming from?" "I . . ." I had no idea where it was coming from. "I mean, after all these crazy stories he made up about your brother, you are still friends." "What do you mean by 'crazy stories'?" he asked. "I mean that he was telling everyone Richard got in a fight with him, punched him in the face, then he told the whole world Richard was married." I stopped and looked at him. There was something in his eyes, he seemed annoyed with my questions. "As far as I know, Richard did punch him in the face." "He wouldn't," I said, smirking. "Obviously, you don't know my brother, and he can be quite violent." I didn't say anything to that. "And as far as a marriage rumor goes, let me ask you: how is it any of your business?" "I . . . it was my business!" I objected. "Whatever, I don't want to talk about my brother," he said and went up the stairs. "Let's find Max and get out of here," he said to me, looking for him. "Max?" I asked. "Why do we need to find him?" The idea wasn't appealing to me. "I promised to give him a ride."

Despite all the fun I'd had hanging with Kai, it was getting more awkward by the second. First that Linda and now Max. How much more unpleasant company could I take? We drove in silence, the air in the car was so thick one could cut it with a knife. Thank God it was a short ride.

"Sleepy?" Kai asked me when I started to yawn in the elevator. "No," I said shortly, then leaned into him and kissed him passionately. Oh, how I missed that. "I know a couple of activities for a good night's sleep," he said and kissed me back.

When it comes to sex, I can't think of anyone I have ever had better chemistry with than Kai. He was that guy I could never say no to.

We had wild sex all night, and when I was finally able to get some sleep, he woke me up ready for another round. Everything was great, sex was great, Kai was great, and I always felt great about myself with him.

"I'm going to have lunch with my mom," I heard Kai saying from the shower as I lay in bed checking my Insta feed. "Yeah?" I said lazily. "I'm picking her up at 12:30 . . . wanna come?" "I think I just did," I said, winking at him when he walked into the bedroom and gave me a kiss. "I'm serious. Do you want to have lunch with us?" Meeting his mom? Who was also Richard's mom, and whom I'd met a month ago? "I don't think it's a good idea," I said. "Well, up to you. I shouldn't be gone for long; do you want to hang around? Wait for me?" He'd never asked me to stay at his place alone before, and I couldn't quite figure out what had changed.

While he was in the closet getting dressed, I got a text from Tim. We hadn't talked for more than a month, and suddenly he was inviting me out to his friend's birthday party to be his date. I was thinking about whether or not to text him back when Kai asked me for the second time if I was going to wait for him at his apartment. Although I politely passed, he invited me to come over later that day. He was hosting dinner for some of his friends who were visiting LA for a couple of weeks, and he wanted me to be a part of it. "You want to see me twice in one day?" I said sarcastically. "I didn't know I was so welcomed here." He chuckled. "You are always welcome here." I promised to give him an answer later that day.

"You're so cute," he said, kissing me. Then Kai got me an Uber, and I left.

For lunch, Chloe and I went to do a little day-time drinking with cocktails and gossip. Plus, I need-ed professional advice. The big question of the day was should I go to a birthday party with Tim or have dinner with Kai and his friends. I still hadn't given a positive answer to either one. Two hours and three mimosas later, we still couldn't decide, so we took our "daytime drinking" to Chloe's place, turning it into "afternoon drinking" first and into "nighttime drink-ing" later.

The next morning when I checked my phone, I had dozens of missed calls and text messages from both guys. While they were waiting for my response, I had been passed out on my friend's couch. Surpris-ingly, I didn't feel any regrets and didn't even want to text back either one of them.

The next week I spent with my friends by the pool. After five days of not returning Kai's calls, he stopped contacting me, and I decided it was for the best. I thought I should really put myself out there and give it a real chance, maybe meet someone new, flirt, date, maybe even fall in love. It seemed like the right time.

On Sunday, Chloe took me to a Hollywood Hills house party. "I thought it could be a great place to meet someone," she said, pulling into the driveway to park her car. "There will be all kinds of guys, and the best part, no one we have ever dated." "Well, that is a huge plus," I said with a straight face, and we both giggled.

We got our hopes and expectations up and went straight inside to meet cute, intelligent, funny, and, most importantly, new guys. But thirty minutes in, there was still no sign of anyone who fit the description. That house was full of dull, narcissistic men in their forties and a bunch of fuckboys.

"I gotta say, this party sucks!" I said, disappointed. "We can leave any second," Chloe reassured me, "but let's stay for a while; maybe someone will show up!" We agreed on that, but secretly I had lost all hope already. "Another half an hour, and we are leaving!" I said while looking around. "Deal! I'll get us drinks." Chloe walked to the bar. At least they had good food and beverages at that house.

"By the look on your face, I can say you hate this party," I heard a deep voice say and turned. His name was Adam. He was a 33-year-old junior partner in a law firm, and the moment I met him, I knew I was in trouble. "Excuse me?" I said, smiling. "I'm Adam." "Sophie."

We talked all evening. I had to admit it was nice to find a man you could talk to, and not just small talk, but have a real conversation with. We exchanged numbers, and he invited me on a date for Friday night.

On my way home, Kai called me three times. I

didn't answer and never returned his calls. I had finally turned the page and started a new chapter in my life, the chapter called Adam.

XII

NOT HEARTLESS, JUST USING MY HEART LESS

Have you ever looked at a person and instantly known from the very beginning you two were meant for each other? After everything I had put myself through with Richard, I wasn't going to rush into a new relationship, but then I met him—six-two, deep, dark eyes, and a smile one could conquer the world with.

We had known each other only for three weeks, but I felt like we were somehow connected. I was really falling for Adam, and I knew he felt the same way. Although we had known each other for only a short time, I had already met his close friends and his sister, but more importantly, unlike Richard, he wasn't afraid to talk about his feelings.

"Do you believe in soulmates?" he asked one day over dinner. "I do, why?" "Because I feel that you are my soulmate. I look at you and feel things I have never felt before, and it scares me, but on some level, I know that we are so right for each other." I was speechless. Not once in my life had I met a man who spoke so openly.

We had been dating for almost a month and still hadn't had sex. To be honest, he was probably the first person I had lasted that long with. With Richard, I jumped into bed on a first date, but this time with Adam, I wanted to wait and make the first experience memorable for both of us. I was finally in a mature relationship. He was a lawyer in his early thirties with a great ocean-view apartment, great personality, and no commitment issues. What else can a girl ask for?! Everything seemed perfect, even too perfect, and as a wise woman once said, "If he seems too good to be true, he probably is."

Because then I didn't hear from him for three days, and when I called, it went straight to voice mail. He didn't return my call for the whole week. I didn't know what to think—maybe he was just busy, or maybe he had a family emergency, or maybe he got sick.

On Friday, Chloe and I were heading to this big party. We had been planning it for the previous two months. I had told Adam about it, and he had been excited to come with us and bring few friends along, but now, since he ghosted me, it was just Choe and me.

The second we walked into the club, I saw at

least a dozen friends and frenemies. As we were trying to make our way to the bar, we met three cute
guys, and even though I was still upset about Adam,
the night wasn't looking so dull after all. We got our
cocktails and were on our way back to the DJ's table
when I crashed into someone and spilled a drink all
over myself. I looked up and froze for a second. There
he was, Adam, after a week of silence, all dressed up
and with a glass of whiskey, neat, in his hand. "Chloe,
hi," he said and kissed my friend on the cheek without paying any attention to me. "Where are you guys
going?" he asked, and before we answered, added, "I
have a table, come join us." "We will think about it," I
said bitterly, then took Chloe's hand and, pulling her,
walked away. "What are you doing? Let's go to their
table" she said when we were far enough away that
Adam wouldn't hear anything. "No!" I said shortly.
She knew it was impossible to change my mind and
let it go at that point.

Half an hour later, we were at the table of our
good friend, who also happened to be the club owner.
I was having so much fun that I almost forgot about
Adam. I felt my phone vibrating in my purse, and
when I took it out, there were four texts from Adam:
'Are you coming to my table?', 'Where are you' 'Just
tell me if you are coming', 'I need to know.' "Let's go,"
I said to Chloe all of a sudden. "Where?" "Adams table." I rolled my eyes, and she giggled.

"Sophie," Adam said, smiling, surprised to see
me. "You texted me, here I am," I said with a fake ar-

rogance. The rest of the evening we spent together. I danced with Adam and Chloe with his best friend, who had fallen for her charm right away.

After the party was over and everyone was about to be kicked out of the club, I saw Adam talking to a girl, but I didn't say anything. When we were already outside waiting for an Uber, he brought it up himself. "That girl, she is a friend of my sister." "Who?" I pretended like I didn't even notice anything. "The girl I talked to. I know her all the way from Texas, way back when we lived there; she and my sister used to be best friends," he explained. "Oh, don't worry, that's cool," I said and tried to force a smile. "Right . . . I just wanted to explain." "You don't need to explain anything to me," I said, but I was happy he did. I didn't want to have what I had with Richard, constant jealousy of one another, and suspicion, but what if all the guys I picked were the same type?

The four of us went to Adam's friend's house. They opened a bottle of champagne, and after I was drunk enough, I started talking. "So, tell me, mister lawyer, where have you been for the past seven days?" He took my hand, pulled me closer, and kissed me. "I had to think," he said. "Think? Think about what?" I said quite loudly, but the rest of the party was either polite enough or drunk enough not to pay attention. "To think about what I want right now. I'm getting all these feelings, and I don't know if I want a relationship." I couldn't listen to that anymore; I was too scared of the words I knew he was about to say, so I stopped him from saying them with a kiss. The rest of the night, we made out. "Take me home," I whispered to him. "OK, I'll get you an Uber," Adam said and pulled out his phone. "No . . . take me to your place," I said, kissing him. For a second there, it seemed he wasn't sure if he even wanted to. "Yes, let's go!" he finally said.

The next morning, he was in a rush to get rid of me. An excuse for that was his urgent need to go to a friend's place to pick up stuff he left there the night before. He got me an Uber, walked to the car, kissed me, opened the car door, and said, "I'll call you soon," and on that note, I left his place, to which I was never invited again.

I didn't hear from him during the next week, so I decided to take the matter into my own hands and give him a friendly call to remind him of my existence. He seemed off when we talked. It was a different Adam, very cold, very distant, it seemed he wanted to end our talk as soon as possible. "We'll talk soon," he said and then hung up. Of course, we didn't. I tried to get in touch with him, but he simply ignored all of my texts and calls, and then, two weeks later, I ran into him in the day club. Not only did he pretend he didn't know me, but he was flirting with every girl there. It was torture. What was it? What kind of a sick joke? Could he have been lying the whole time we had been together? All those heavy words about us being soulmates, about feelings and connection, could it be his move to hit on girls and get into their panties?

I didn't know, but I felt like a complete fool who had fallen for yet another fuckboy and developed feelings for him in a short period of time. I couldn't help it; tears ran down my eyes like Niagara Falls. I couldn't breathe, couldn't make a sound. I was having a panic attack. All my dating life in LA was coming back to me in flashbacks. Was it even possible to find a nice guy in this city? Or was it my fate to continue to choose assholes, falling for them, having my heart broken, and then restarting? Was it my personalized "circle of life"? Or was I simply in the wrong city, a city where true love didn't exist?

While this was all going on in my head, he and his friends made an approach, and while they all seemed friendly and polite, asking about my week, my well-being, and my work, Adam didn't even look at me, not even once. Instead, he was hugging some girl he just met and offering to ditch the place and continue to party at his place. As I was holding back my tears, I noticed a cute guy in the crowd looking at me. At that moment I knew this was the only chance I had to save face. So, I looked over and smiled right back at him. It didn't take long before he came over to me. "Excuse me," he said. "Hi. I'm Sophie." "Dan." He smiled at me, and I felt so much kindness coming from him. It was exactly what I needed at that moment. He was smart, a nice guy, and more importantly, he was honest. That night I left with him.

Even though I liked Dan, I couldn't help but feel tricked and used by Adam. Was it my ego and pride that wouldn't allow me to let go, or was it because I fell in love with him? I couldn't tell the difference anymore. I was obsessed with him, and he seemed to cut me off entirely, which only made it worse for me. I became one of those crazy, desperate girls I used to laugh at. At every party, every dinner, every gathering, I was looking for him and him alone. I was stalking him on social media, and meanwhile, I had this nice, honest, great guy who wanted to be with me. Someone who wasn't playing, wasn't using me. Maybe I got so used to being hurt I couldn't live without it. Maybe a person who wasn't constantly causing me pain couldn't get my interest. Maybe I was simply a masochist.

After a month of Dan trying to get closer and me rejecting and simply not noticing him in my mad chase after Adam, he gave up on me and decided that if I couldn't move on with him, he would without me. It was a wake-up call, which I naturally chose to ignore. I was still not over Adam, and as it turned out, I was definitely not over Richard either.

Summer 2018 was by far the wildest of my life. One night, Chloe convinced me it was time to live a little, and in this attempt, we ended up at the Highlight Room. Intoxicated with alcohol and heat, I did something I had never done before. I saw a hot guy, I walked over to him, and I just kissed him.

"Wow," I heard him saying. He was holding my waist. We were still standing close to each other, so close I felt his boner. "Take me home," I said, looking into his eyes and just like that, not even knowing his name. He only looked at me, smiled, then took my hand and led the way. When we walked outside, he was still holding my hand. I didn't even know his name, and I was about to get in the car with him to go God knows where, and at that particular moment, it didn't bother me even for a second. He was ordering Uber when the flower lady approached us. The next thing I knew, I was holding a bouquet. "Thanks," I said, kissing him. It was a nice gesture, especially when he already knew I was gonna sleep with him. But he didn't stop there. When the car arrived, he opened the door for me, and when we got to the apartment, he played piano to impress me.

It was nice, romantic even, if you are willing to forget for a second that we two had only just met.

Two hours later, I pulled up my shorts, grabbed my shoes, and was already on my way out. "Thanks again. It was fun," I said, sneaking out the door, and when I was already halfway out, I heard footsteps behind me. "Wait, I don't even know your name." I turned around and smiled at him. "You don't need to, that's fine, let's not pretend it's something that it's not." I was ready to turn and walk away. "Can I see you again?" I took a breath and then spilled. "I'm sorry if I wasn't clear, but I don't want to see you again." And just like that I walked away, got in an Uber, and never saw the guy after that. Until this day his name is still a mystery to me.

The next morning, surprisingly, I woke up feeling very good about myself. For the first time, I was in control. That night changed the game. I decided it was time to live the way I wanted and not the way society was telling me to. My schedule had never been busier, and even though that particular summer I was jobless, I managed to have lunches and dinners at the fanciest restaurants in town almost every single day. Sometimes I had ten dates in a week, and the funniest thing... the more I rejected them, the more those guys got attached to me. I didn't sleep with every one of them, but the number of people I slept with that summer was still pretty big. Doctors, investment bankers, lawyers, businessmen—that summer I dated them all, and many actually wanted to get serious, and yet I felt like my heart wasn't open to that. I wasn't in the right place to be attached to anyone and had no idea if I ever would be able to move on. I was going on dates with this whole bunch of guys—nice, good looking, successful guys—and felt nothing but sexual desire, and after I had them, nothing . . . again.

By the end of July, I decided for myself I was done with dating. I was going to focus on me, my needs, my career, myself. After all, there was no man who could make my heart start racing again no matter how hard I looked for him. Then on August 1, when I was at home enjoying my carefree Sunday afternoon, I heard my phone buzzing. I picked it up

and saw his 'I miss you' text, and my heart stopped
and then started to race like never before.

XIII

YOUR PARADISE IS WHERE I AM

Richard Corbin. This man has caused me lots of pain in his day, and yet some of my happiest memories are linked to him. They say where there is love, there is pain. In my mind, I knew that our relationship wasn't ideal, that maybe we were even toxic for each other, but in my heart, I loved him more than I had ever loved anyone before.

After his text, I couldn't stop thinking about him and our time together. It seemed that no matter where we were or who we were with, we would find a way back into each other's lives eventually. After a week of texting each other back and forth, he told me he was coming back to Los Angeles after six months in Europe and asked if I would be interested in meeting him for lunch or dinner. I realized at that moment Adam and all those men after him were nothing but a distraction from the one I really wanted all that time. Maybe that was the reason I got so hung up on Adam in the first place; I had needed a way out, and he was exactly that for me, a chance to move on. But no matter how hard I tried, I could never get Richard out of my system. After all that time, I was still utterly in love with him.

The next couple of weeks passed by, and I couldn't wait to finally see Richard again. He was coming back on September 1, and while I was planning what to wear, how to look, what to say, he was texting me the sweetest things, saying how much he missed me during our time apart and how much he wanted to try again. That's when I knew he had changed, and that he had changed for the better. The question was, had I also changed, and if yes, was it a good thing?

During summer, I let myself relax and enjoy the time off. I'd quit my job in June and lived off whatever I had saved in my bank account. But by the end of August, I felt it was finally time to put myself out there again and find a job. So that was exactly what I did. I got an interview through my friend's friend, and after just thirty minutes of friendly face-to-face conversation, I had a job. Everything seemed to be finally falling into place. Job, career, love life—it was a cue to a celebrate.

I knew what I wanted with Richard, it was a committed relationship, so while we were still separated by a thousand miles and an ocean, I felt it was my last chance to go out and enjoy a night as a single gal. And that was exactly what Chloe and I did.

On Sunday, Richard finally got to LA. He called me straight from the airport and was eager to meet me that exact same day. Because of the twelve-hour flight and jet lag, we decided not to go out but to meet at his place instead. At six o'clock he got me an Uber, and as I got in the car, I asked the driver about the address we were going to, and when he answered my question, I felt as if my blood had frozen inside my body. We were going to Kai's place. At once, thoughts started swirling through my mind. Theories, fears, absurd ideas, I was getting them all. As we were approaching the building, I texted Richard, asking for the apartment number. It was the exact same apartment I'd visited three months ago. What if it was some kind of a test? What if Richard didn't care about me and it was just a plan to get me there to humiliate me for sleeping with Kai . . . again. I was scared to death. Why did I ever meet with Kai again? What for? I regretted it so much at that moment and blamed myself for ruining my own life with just one night of weakness.

At that point, I didn't know Kai's whereabouts, and the mere thought of what might happen if he was also in that apartment made me anxious. "We are here," I heard the driver say. It was too late to back down? I walked inside the lobby, where I was greeted by the concierge. I told him the apartment number, and he walked me to the elevator. Everything there was so well known. I had spent some of my best nights at that place. As the elevator was moving up, I started to get more and more anxious. Mixed emotions of excitement, fear, and curiosity all hit me simultaneously, but then the elevator finally opened, I got out, and as I started to walk that long corridor, I saw a figure right at the end of it. Excitement and joy overwhelmed me; no more fear and anxiety were left in me, only excitement. I started to walk faster and faster until the point where I was already running toward Richard. When I got close enough, I saw his face, full of love and kindness. I almost jumped into his arms. "I've missed you," I heard his voice softly saying. "I've missed you more!" I whispered and kissed him.

All my worries were in vain. Not only did Richard not know about the night I spent at that apartment, but Kai wasn't even in Los Angeles at that time, so I could breathe freely.

Kai and I had an amazing love life, the sex was so intense and so wild I thought I would never experience anything better, but that was until that night with Richard. That night, for the first time ever, I truly understood the well-known phrase "making love." My feelings for Richard were so great it almost hurt to bear them. That night was the moment I knew I truly loved him. Next to him, in his arms, I finally found the peace I had searched for. I was in paradise, my very own heaven on Earth.

The next morning, I woke up smelling fresh toast and coffee. Richard was making breakfast. "Good morning," I said as I walked into the kitchen. "Good morning." He leaned over the counter to kiss me. "Coffee?" he asked, and when I opened my mouth to answer, he continued to make an impression on me. "I don't drink coffee," he teased, smiling, then added, "I know, I remember." "Good to know you're staying true to yourself and don't change your habit of teasing me," I said sarcastically, pouring myself a glass of water. He smiled and put a plate in front of me. "Here you go, milady." On the plate were two slices of toast with neatly sliced heart-shaped strawberries and some jam. It was the cutest little thing. "Let us try this culinary masterpiece." I took a bite. "Mmmm, my compliments to the chef," I continued and smiled at him. "So, how was Europe?"

"Not too bad," Richard replied, without giving me any details. "And what did you do for six months?" I continued. "Well, I went for work, I told you." It seemed he wasn't very willing to talk about it, and that only made me more curious. "Six months is a long time; did you meet someone while there?" I asked, sipping my water, anxiously waiting for a response. "No." His short answer made me angry. "Are you really expecting me to believe that you haven't slept with anyone from the last time we saw each other up till now?" I asked aggressively. "Yes, I do, actually, because it's the truth." I looked at him, raising my eyebrow. "Why does it even matter?" he asked me, and for a second there, I was ready to start a fight, but I controlled my emotions. After all, did it really matter? He was with me now, and he obviously missed me, so why ruin everything with an argument. "It doesn't," I said, trying to convince myself. "If you say there was no one, then I believe you." I forced a smile, but deep down, I knew he was lying to me. I felt it in my gut. But I decided not to focus on the past and just look into the future. The two of us had a chance for a clean start. After everything we had been through, after everything we had said to each other, we still had a chance to make things right. And that day was a clean start, not only for Richard and me, but also as my first day at a new job. Richard gave me a ride to work that morning, and we made plans to see each other later that evening. He was taking me to dinner at Katana to celebrate my first day in a new position. That evening was great. Richard got me flowers, bought me a fancy dinner at my favorite restaurant—he was a perfect gentleman. And I hadn't even noticed how I had started to compare him to all the other men I had been with in the past months. It made me see things clearer. Not only was Richard so much better than anyone else, but he was also working on becoming a better version of himself, and I couldn't help but love him even more for that.

The next couple of weeks were fantastic. It was a well-balanced, very mature, healthy relationship. I couldn't have been happier. It was so obvious we had done a huge job—we changed, we grew, we became more patient toward one another. It was a nice change in our dynamic.

"Did you notice how different things are?" Richard asked me one day when we were in bed, cuddling and watching a romantic comedy. "The fact that you agreed to watch a movie I picked is a huge change indeed," I teased him. "No, but really, I was the biggest asshole, mistreating people . . ." he stopped for a second and then continued, " . . . mistreating you." "True, and yes, I did notice how different things are, and I do believe that maybe this time we both changed for good!" We were happy, and we believed that time it would last . . . if only.

XIV

LOVE IS PATIENT, LOVE IS KIND, LOVE ENVIES NOT . . .

Love . . . what is it really? Is there really a thing as "unconditional" love? Or is it just fiction, a creation of our own imagination? Something we simply make ourselves believe in. From birth, the world teaches us about love through fairy tales, movies, books, but can one really love with love so pure, so innocent, without an agenda, without a thought of one's own good? Can love really be unconditional? In our world, to love someone means to declare to the rest that this person is now yours, and if someone else is threatening to take them away from us, love is replaced with jealousy.

Some say jealousy is a disease, and if so, Richard and I are two patients who can never be cured.

Things with Richard were good . . . for a month or so. After that, we started to pick fights with each other, and I thought some time off would be good for us. After all, we saw each other almost every day. Perhaps a week or two apart would help us. I recommended it, and he accepted. It was a good change, and I finally had time to spend with friends, but Richard didn't seem to be a big fan of that change after all. I'd always known him to be jealous, territorial, possessive, and manipulative, but I had no idea how much until the night when Chloe and I went out for dinner and ended up meeting my very close friend Liam, whom I knew from school.

We had spent the night drinking and taking selfies together. One of those pics I posted on my IG story, and in a couple of seconds, Richard texted me a reply, 'You are hilarious! Every night a different guy lol.' I was drunk, and it seemed funny to me at the time, and I texted back, 'Haha, first and foremost, he is my friend, and he is gay lol.' 'Everyone is gay,' he responded. 'What does it even mean?' But he only texted, 'Never mind' and then 'Later.' I had no idea what he was trying to say, and at that point, I was drunk and pissed off. Everything seemed so good between us when we were together, but the moment I started to pay attention to some else besides him, Richard started to become possessive. I was so angry with him. 'Yeah, never mind! Learn what's going on first before texting some bullshit. Enjoy your night,' I texted, wanting to have the last word in it, but so did he—'Safe sex, later!'

After that, we didn't speak or text each other's for the whole week. I was very mad, but apparently, he was too. Then, on Friday, he replied to my IG story again. I posted a view from my bedroom window, and he texted, 'You are not out yet? Wow. Soon to be at a club lol.' To that, I only said that I wasn't going anywhere and got nothing in response.

The next evening, I got another text from Richard on my IG. 'Where are u chilling tonight?' 'Home, most likely,' was my response. To that he sent me three laughing emoji and then a text, 'Sure you will.' I was tired of his sarcasm and his drama, and I chose to ignore his bitter comments.

Later that evening some of my friends invited me for a quick dinner at Tao. It was a small group, but everyone was bringing a date. I didn't want to be the only loser there and show up alone, plus it was a great excuse to finally get on Richard's good side. I texted him the details, saying I was heading to Tao in an hour and was hoping to see him there. 'Of course, you are, I had no doubt in my mind' was not a response I expected. 'Enjoy.' I felt so angry, so annoyed at the moment. It was a gesture. I was trying to make up, and what for? I asked myself, what was I doing? What was the point of this whole charade? And was it even worth it?' The answer was no, so I texted him a long text. 'You know, I'm trying to be patient because by now I know you pretty well, to understand that sometimes you don't mean all the crazy shit you say, but it's not an easy task. You keep treating me like I'm your property and not a human being. No matter how I feel about you, it's obvious by now that you and I are toxic, and all we bring into each other lives is drama. So, I say, let's move on, and this time for good.' 'Sure. It's Saturday, I wouldn't expect anything different. Get lucky and enjoy' was all I got. To straighten things up, once and for all, I called him. "What is your problem?" I asked aggressively as soon as he picked up. "What's with all the sarcasm?" He didn't say anything, so I continued, "If you have trust issues, whose fault is that?" "I was right," he started, "I knew you could not stay home, and you didn't." He took a deep breath and then continued, "Also, of course, I have issues trusting someone who slept with my brother after sleeping with me, are you kidding me?" For a second there, I couldn't find any words at all, but as we all well know, the best defense is a good offense. "Well, I was the one who told you about Kai, wasn't I?! I could have just never brought it up, and you wouldn't even found out. And why not walk away from me the second you learned it, huh? I have made one mistake, and you keep treating me like shit ever since." "One mistake?" he interrupted me. "Just go enjoy your night and keep up the good work. I know how you are when you get drunk, you can fuck a horse!" "Don't you ever talk to me like that!" I exploded, "or it will be the last time we talk!" "Fine." His voice sounded calm and confident. "Fine!" I repeated and then hung up. I felt as though I had a hurricane inside of me ready to get out and destroy anyone and anything that got in its way. I was mad at him, at myself, and the whole world. That night I stayed home, and Richard got his way, again.

In two days, when Richard and I both cooled down, he called and apologized. I accepted, and we started over. No matter what he did, no matter how mad he made me, it seemed I could never really be free of him. We were two magnets pushing and pulling back together. I knew that he probably would never trust me entirely because of my poor choices in the past, but I was willing to deal with that. He was jealous of me, and jealousy is a sign of love, is it not? Richard had this idea that all my actions were nothing else but a reflection of Chloe's influence on me. He was utterly against me going out literally anywhere with her. Richard made sure I was always by his side; he wanted to know and control my every move, and I believed this to be the definition of love. Month after month, it was just Richard and me, and I was completely fine with that. At least we were not fighting anymore, and if all it took was to be with him all the time, then I would do exactly that. My routine was simple: I worked until 6;00 p.m., then Richard picked me up, we got takeout, watched a movie, went to bed, and then woke up and repeated. My wild weekends turned into movie and cooking nights. My Sunday hangovers into walks, lunches, and hikes. I lived a married life without actually being married. We practically lived together.

Months had passed, and it was time for my birthday. That year I wanted simplicity, only closest friends, only those I loved. "So look, I have been thinking," I said to Richard on one of our Sunday mornings together, "this year I want it to be just you and me for my actual birthday, and then we can go have brunch together with the girls the next day.

What do you think?" "I might have to go to San Francisco that weekend," he said casually, looking at his phone. "On my birthday?" People who knew me also knew how important all holidays were to me, and my birthday celebration made the top of the list, so the fact that the person I loved the most didn't even care enough to be there on that day came as a bit of an unpleasant surprise. "Yes, it's for work," he explained. I didn't say a word but got upset, and apparently, he felt it, because instantly he added, "But if I do, I'll try my best to get back in time," and, putting his phone away, smiled at me. "Promise?" I asked enthusiastically. "Yes, promise." And with that promise, I began to make plans. I made a brunch reservation, leaving the dinner reservation to Richard, assuming he would surprise me with something special.

Three days before my birthday, he flew to San Francisco, reassuring me he would be back for the occasion.

On Friday, I woke up hearing a balloon blowing up. I got up and went to the living room to check what was going on. "Happy Birthday!" A bunch of balloons and confetti were thrown at my face as I walked in. "Happy Birthday!" Chloe and Mia kept on yelling. My whole living room was decorated with flowers and birthday-themed decorations. The day started great, and I was positive it would only get better. At 11:00 a.m. I got a bunch of calls, texts, and DMs from almost everyone I knew—everyone but one person. Richard still didn't make any approach, and I was dying to see what he got for me. But then, at noon, I received a short text, 'Happy Birthday, sweetie!' Obviously, he was planning something, I just couldn't figure out what. But when at 3:00 p.m. I didn't get flowers or even a phone call, I slowly started to doubt if he was planning anything at all. At 6:00 p.m. when I heard a ring, his name appeared on the screen, and as I picked up he started singing, "Happy birthday to you, happy birthday to you, happy birthday dear Sophie . . ." "Hi," I said without any enthusiasm. "Cheer up, it's your birthday!" "It's good that you remember." I couldn't have hidden my frustration even if I'd wanted to. "You told me you were gonna make it back to LA in time, where are you?" "I rented a car and am driving back right now." "A car?" I got even more frustrated. "You are taking a seven-hour drive when you could fly in?" I asked him with irritation. "I got stuck, and I'm driving because of you." "Oh, so I need to be grateful? Is that what you're saying? Grateful for being ditched on my birthday?" I was furious. "Look, just go have dinner with some friends, and I'll pick you up around midnight." My pulse was accelerating. "I can't! Don't you understand?" "I understand that you are making a big deal out of something so stupid!" Though he sounded calm, I knew he was angry. "It is a big deal for me because I wanted to be with you on my birthday. But obviously, you don't give a shit! You know what, don't bother calling me when you are in LA!" After that, I hung up, dropped my phone, crawled into bed, and cried hysterically for a good hour.

"How's our birthday girl doing?" was the first thing Chloe asked when I called her. "I'm . . ." I started but didn't know what to say, then I sniffled, and she knew right away something was wrong. "What happened?" she asked me. "Oh, nothing much, just got ditched on my birthday, and now I'm drinking champagne in my PJ's," I tried to joke. "What do you mean ditched? What happened to your plans with Richard?" "Well, apparently, I was the only one who had plans," I sniffled again. "He is still in San Francisco." "He's not coming?" "Well, he is. He was driving when we talked," I explained. "It's fine, you'll see him tomorrow, and tonight I'll be your date," she said, trying to cheer me up. "No, I don't want to go anywhere." I paused, trying to pull myself together and not cry. "I'll stay in and see you tomorrow at brunch." "Are you sure? Do you want me to come over?" Chloe asked. "That's fine, I'm going to bed soon."

After I talked to Chloe, I decided to finish the bottle of champagne, get drunk, and watch all the Bridget Jones movies. When I had just turned on Bridget Jones Part 2, Richard called. For a moment there I didn't know whether or not I should pick up. "What?" "I'm sorry," he said. "I've spent my birthday in bed crying, so thank you." "I'm outside, and it's still your birthday for another fifteen minutes, we can celebrate." "Oh, I've got enough celebrations for one day, thank you very much." I was bouncing between sad and furious. "Come on, come outside." I was exhausted from all the crying, but I didn't want to sleep alone that night, so I changed from my PJ's into sweatpants and a hoodie and went to meet him. As soon as he saw me, he got out of the car. "Happy Birthday!" he said and spread his arms, trying to hug me. Despite everything, I was happy to see him, so I gave in and leaned closer, placing my head on his chest. "I've missed you," he said, kissing my forehead.

I woke up the next morning at his place. Right next to my pillow, there was a little Tiffany box. I instantly grabbed it and heard him giggling. "Good morning," he said, smiling. As I was impatiently unpacking my present, he, also impatiently, was waiting for my reaction. I gasped in delight—inside was a pendant on a tiny gold chain with my name on it. "I love it! I absolutely love it!" I smiled and almost jumped on Richard with a hug. "I'm wearing it today to brunch," I said, trying the pendant on. "Oh, which reminds me, I gotta go home to get ready." "Can't you get ready here? We can go together." "My dress is at home, plus girls wanted to pick me up," I said, getting up and walking to the mirror to check my new pendant. "It's going to be just four of us?" Richard asked, going to the bathroom. "Well, no, it's going to be five of us, actually." "Five?" he repeated, turning the water on in the shower. "My friend, you don't know him." "Him?" He sounded nervous. "Yes, him," I said, walking into the bathroom after Richard. "He is my very good friend, so please behave." "I always do," he said and smiled. "Well, one can argue," I teased him. "Oh, and we all know you love to argue," Richard laughed, and I rolled my eyes at him without saying anything.

"Reservation for five—under Sophie," I said, walking over to the hostess stand. "Is all of your party here?" "Not yet." I smiled, hoping she would like me and give us the best table. "Just the three of us for now." "Oh," she said, "you may wait for the rest of your guests at the bar." As she said it, I saw Richard at the door and raised my hand, waving at him. "We are four now, actually." "OK, would you like to be seated or wait for one more person?" "We'll get a table and wait for him there, thank you." My attempts to charm her were not in vain. She gave us a beautiful round table right in the middle of the restaurant. As we were sitting down, my friend Liam noticed us and walked over. "Hi, birthday girl!" he said, hugging me and kissing me on the cheek. Then he handed me a huge bouquet of white roses. "Aw, aren't you sweet," I said, smiling. "I don't think you have met my boyfriend," I said, turning to Richard. "This is Richard, and this is my friend Liam. We know each other all the way from school." "It is very nice to meet you," Liam said with a big smile on his face, reaching for a handshake. "Pleasure," Richard said, but his face was saying the completely opposite thing. "You'll sit next to me, babe?" I asked him, sitting down. "Yeah, sure."

Brunch was going great until Liam, who was very talkative and friendly, raised a question. "So, Sophie, my darling, what did you do yesterday?" "I . . ." I paused, having no idea what to answer, ". . . ahem, I stayed in, actually." "You stayed home? On your birthday?" Liam sounded surprised. "Well, Richard and I wanted to spend my birthday together, but he had to go to San Francisco for work," I said and glanced at Richard. "I asked her out, but she was too upset to go anywhere," Chloe, who never liked Richard very much, and ever since he'd become so opposed to the two of us hanging out now openly disliked, added. "She cried for hours," she said reproachfully and then looked at Richard. "It doesn't matter," I said, trying to clear the air, "we are all here now and celebrating," I said, sipping my mimosa and trying to change the topic. "Here, cheers to me!" I said, raising my glass.

The rest of the brunch wasn't as joyful as it had been in the beginning. Immediately after the cake was served, Richard called over our waiter. "Check, please," he said and reached for his wallet. "We are not leaving yet," I protested. "I've got to go," he said, taking out his credit card. "I'm meeting someone." "Can it wait?" I raised my eyebrow, staring at him. His behavior was shocking. "No, it's important. Do you wanna come with me?" I didn't know what to say. I couldn't just leave my friends, and I didn't want to. "I was thinking we'll go somewhere else after brunch," I said, then paused. "It's my birthday . . ." "Your birthday was yesterday," he said with an iron-cold voice. "Are you coming with or no?" he asked again. "I . . . I'm going to stay with my friends, and maybe you can join us after your meeting?" I asked. "Yeah, maybe." Then he noticed my friends were taking out their credit cards. "No worries, I've got it," he said and took the check. "It's nice to meet you, Liam. Girls, nice seeing you." He stood up, and so did I. "I'll see you later?" I asked him. He just nodded, then I tried to kiss him, but instead, he gave me a hug and then left. I didn't know how to behave. I sat down, putting on a fake smile, trying to pretend nothing had happened. "Is everything OK?" Mia asked. "Yeah, everything is fine." I stopped for a second—truth be told, I had no idea if everything was fine. "Should we go to the Waldorf after?" They all agreed, and thirty minutes later, we were on our way. I took a car with Chloe and Mia went with Liam.

"So, what really happened earlier?" Chloe asked as soon as we were alone. "Honestly, I don't know. But I wanted to ask you to be nicer to Richard." "Me? Unlike him, I'm always nice," she protested. "It just seems that you guys are always looking for a reason to fight." "Or maybe it's him and his control over you," she said, irritated. "He is manipulating you, and he is obviously against us hanging out! I never see you anymore, my best friend. It would be one thing if you were in a happy, healthy relationship, but you are not, and you know it!" "What is this, an intervention?" I asked her, annoyed. "Maybe we should have one," Chloe said in a very serious voice, and then we looked at each other and started giggling.

"He still hasn't texted?" Liam asked me when he noticed I was constantly checking my phone. "No, he hasn't," I answered, trying not to look too worried. "Can I be honest, Sophie?" "Depends on what you are going to say," I said and smiled. "Why are you with this guy?" He continued, "Clearly, he doesn't care enough, otherwise you would be his priority." "What gives you the right to say that?" I snapped. "I'm sorry, but I only say it because you are my friend." Liam sounded very genuine. I had known him for almost ten years, and in those ten years, he had been nothing but a good, caring friend, though sometimes a little too nosy. "I need a drink, excuse me." I stood up and went to the bar. Mia followed me. "Hey, is everything OK?" she asked, placing her hand on my shoulder. "It's just really annoying that everyone assumes they know Richard or our relationship, and they constantly judge us." "You're right," Mia started, "we don't know him, or what your relationship is like, it's only between you and him, and if you say that everything is good and you are happy, then we are happy for you." She smiled, and I felt relieved. "Thank you," I said, smiling back at her. Mia was older than the rest of us, and also wiser, and she always knew exactly what to say and how to calm Chloe or me down.

I got myself a glass of champagne, and we headed toward our table. I sat down and checked my phone. I had two texts, the first one from my friend who was throwing a party and had invited me to it, the second was much less pleasant. 'Thanks for choosing your friends over me,' Richard had texted me. "Guys, I need to make a phone call," I said to my friends and went downstairs to the lobby to talk to him.

"What's up?" he asked when I called. "Well, what's going on? What was that text about?" I asked him. "You chose to stay with your friends when I asked you to leave with me, and now you are asking what's wrong. You kidding me?" He sounded mad. "Listen, I don't want to fight, that's why I'm calling. Can we not fight at least today, please?" He took a breath and then said OK. "My friend is throwing a party later tonight, I thought maybe we could go." "What friend, do I know them?" Richard sounded very controlling, almost as if he were my boss and I was his employee. "I believe you do; he knows some of your friends" "He?" he asked, irritated. "Yes, he. He who is married and has a kid," I said, tired of Richard's ongoing investigation. "Yes, I think we can check it out." "Cool. I'll call you when I'm done here, OK?" I asked him. "OK."

Forty-five minutes later, we decided to call it a day. We said goodbyes, and Chloe gave me a ride back home. I suddenly felt so exhausted. All the drama, the arguments, drinking, and stress had done a number on me. Chloe pulled over next to my apartment building. "Thanks for the ride." She smiled, and there was some unhidden concern in her smile. "You are always welcome, birthday girl." I stepped out of the car and waved at her as she drove away.

I wanted that day to be over and as soon as I got inside my apartment, I texted Richard that I was not going to the party and suggested we just stay home and watch something. But to my surprise, he wasn't happy to hear that. Instantly he accused me of not wanting to go there with him because I had dated some of the guys who would be at the party, and I didn't want them to know I was taken now. That accusation was the most ridiculous thing I had ever heard. I decided that instead of texting each other back and forth and getting into one of those text messages fights, which Richard seemed to love so much, I would rather just go to his place instead.

In fifteen minutes, I was at the lobby of his building telling the concierge the apartment number I was going to and at the same time in the back of my head thinking how embarrassing it would be if Richard decided he didn't want to see me and the nice Mexican concierge had to tell me to get the hell out of there. Luckily, that didn't happen. After he talked to Richard on the phone and announced my arrival, he told me I was expected. As I got out of the elevator and was walking down the corridor, I started to get some anxiety. I knocked on Richard's door, he opened it the same second, and without saying a word, I walked in. "I don't want to fight," I said to him. "Then don't." He looked at me and then continued. "I got pizza, you hungry?" I nodded.

We had pizza in bed, and then Richard let me pick a movie. Though he always hated my choices, he always agreed to watch them anyway, and I loved that about him.

I fell asleep in the middle of the movie with a slice of pizza on my stomach. Richard didn't wake me up; he cleaned everything, turned the TV off, then spooned me and fell asleep.

During summer, Chloe and I used to go to Bungalow in Santa Monica almost every single Sunday. It was a place one could meet new people, and it was always fun. I thought, why not go there that Sunday, especially after Chloe had told me I had been neglecting my friends ever since getting back together with Richard. And she was perfectly right. I knew it myself, and also knew that it was a chance to make Chloe and Richard like each other and show my friends that even though I was in a relationship, I was still the old me. I texted Chloe, asking her if she wanted to go. She was pretty excited about it and so was I. I was blow-drying my hair after showering when I brought it up with Richard. "I'm thinking of going to Bungalow today, you wanna come?" I asked. "Who else is going?" "Just Chloe, me, and you, if you decide to come along," I said without a second thought and regretted it immediately. "People usually go there to pick up someone," he said judgmentally. "Well, I'm going there to have fun." I smiled. "Right," Richard said, shaking his head as if he didn't believe a single word coming out of my mouth. "Chloe goes to places like this only for one reason," he said. "Well, we are going to have fun, nothing else." "You are going?! After I told you not to?" His voice got very serious. "I invited you to come with, or do you think I would do that if I wanted to meet other guys?" I asked him, arching an eyebrow. "If you go there you can forget about me!" he declared. "This bitch who you call a friend always has this influence on you!" "Don't call her that!" I snapped at him.

"Why not? I call her what she is, and you are the same as her." He looked and me with contempt and then added, "Go on then, go get picked up! You want to be the same whore you were when we met? Go then!" "Oh, fuck that!" I yelled, then grabbed my purse and stormed out of his apartment. I was getting out of the garage when he texted me, 'You go there, and I swear to God, I will never talk to you again!' Then I got another text, but this time from Chloe, asking me what was happening and why my boyfriend was texting her and threatening that if she ever asked me to go with her to "pick-up places" again she would see the consequences, he would make sure of it. Then I got another text from Richard, 'You wanna go out and be the same whore again, in that case, you have no business in my life. And this time I am not joking!' And then another, 'You know what, do whatever you wish. Don't contact me again!' We had some crazy fights over the years but never before had he dragged my friends into them, and that was the line for me. I texted, 'Don't worry, I won't! After you threatened my friend, there is no chance in hell I will ever talk to you again!'

And let me tell you, I've kept my word . . . oh boy, I haven't talked to him for a whole week.

XV

IT'S THE MOST WONDERFUL TIME OF THE YEAR

"Unbelievable arrogance," I said out loud to myself, parking my car. "How dare he? I will never talk to him again after that! Who does he think he is?" All these thoughts were swirling in my head on the day of our fight—it was phase one. "Is he going to apologize or is he expecting me to? He is so fucking arrogant! I won't talk to him until he apologizes!" were my thoughts three days after our fight—that was phase two. "Should I call him myself? He is very stubborn and probably will never make the first move himself . . . Maybe I should call him," I was thinking five days after the fight. On the seventh day, I couldn't take it anymore. I texted Richard myself—that was phase four—and after he didn't reply, I returned back to phase one, deciding I would never ever talk to him again!

At the beginning of December, I felt a need for a break from my obsession with Richard, so I flew home to visit the family. I took four days off and my mom and I did a road trip to the Grand Canyon and did some shopping and dining. It was a perfect trip and some much-needed quality mother-daughter time, and when it seemed I had finally gotten my mind off Richard and had stopped obsessing over him, he suddenly started obsessing over me.

'Hi, when are you coming back to LA,' he texted me when I was on my way to the airport. Someone was obviously all over my Instagram. I really wanted to text him something mean and bitter, but I restrained myself and only texted that I was on my way back. After that, he asked if I would want to meet him, and I agreed to have dinner once I was back in LA. Three days later, we were back together.

Someone once said, "He who has no Christmas in his heart will never find it under a tree." In my family, Christmas has always been a pretty big deal. Traditions, Christmas cooking, tree decorating, presents. I think I could be a 100-year-old lady and still be happy and excited about Christmas. Richard and I both didn't have any family in Los Angeles, and I thought, why not celebrate Christmas together, have a tree, a nice dinner, and all that stuff I had at home. But when I told Richard, he didn't seem to be as enthusiastic as I was about the idea. It turned out he wasn't a big fan of Christmas, and the fact that he would be alone for the holidays this year was actually good news to him. Despite his resistance at first, after all my persuasion, he finally gave in and agreed to spend the holidays my way. I set myself a goal: I would spend December teaching Richard what real

Christmas looked like and would make him love it. Step one was to get us into a joyful mood by watching Christmas movies, lots and lots of them.

"No!" Richard screamed when I was picking our next movie. "No! please . . . we've seen five Christmas movies this week and it's only Wednesday." "That's how you get into the holiday spirit," I protested. "Can we watch something else, please? We always watch what you want. Can I pick something we both will enjoy?" "Pick whatever you want!" I threw the remote on the couch and walked to the bedroom. Five minutes later, I heard Richard's voice. "Come back. You're missing out on a movie." And when I walked in, *A Christmas Carol* was playing on TV. I smiled and sat next to Richard on the couch.

Although he was willing to watch PG-13 movies with me, he still rejected all my other ideas. He didn't go with me to the ballet to see *The Nutcracker* or to the theater to see *A Christmas Carol* or to the Hollywood Christmas Parade, and when I asked him to go with me to my office Christmas party, he declined the invitation.

"If you are not coming, I will ask Chloe!" I told Richard one morning over breakfast, hoping that would change his mind and he would come to the Christmas party with me. "She will be happy to go with me." "Why wouldn't she?" he asked, sipping his espresso. I looked at him, raising an eyebrow. "I'm not going to tolerate your insults towards her." I waited for some bitter comment, but he didn't say a word, and I continued. "She is my friend, like it or not." "Or not," he said without making any eye contact with me. "That's fine, go with her." He then looked at me and added. "But please just come back to my place after." I moved closer to him. "Or you can go with me and then we both come over here." He chuckled, shaking his head.

On Saturday, I woke up at Richard's place and was planning to be out of there by lunch to have enough time to get ready and meet Chloe by 6:30 p.m. and arrive at the restaurant at 7:00 p.m. But my plan was ruined when Richard asked me to stay for lunch. He got me a salad from my favorite place, and I agreed to stay for an extra hour. While we were eating, the lobby called. Evidently, there was a guest downstairs. "Yes, let her in," Richard said to the concierge on the phone. "Her?" I asked. "Yes, my friend is here." I was sitting in my underwear and would have loved to get a heads-up that some "friend" was coming over. I rushed to the bedroom to get some pants. "You could have told me in advance, you know," I said angrily. "She is just dropping off some paperwork," he explained. "What's her name?" I asked, walking back from the bedroom in Richard's sweatpants. I knew I looked ridiculous, and when he saw me Richard smiled. "Nina," he said with unhidden amusement. "Her name is Nina. I'm sure I've told you about her." "I would remember if you did." I was annoyed with him and couldn't hide it. I heard a knock at the door, and before Richard got the chance to open it, I got up from my seat. "I got it!" I said, walking toward the door.

Nina was in her thirties, with long blond hair and hazel eyes. Though it was hard to call her beautiful, she was quite charming. "Hi," I said, opening the door and putting on my most polite and most fake smile. "I'm So—" "Sophie," she finished for me, "I know. I've heard so much about you! It's great to finally meet you." "Oh, have you?" I said sarcastically, turning to Richard. "And your name is..." I looked at Nina from head to toe. "Nina," she said and then kissed me on the cheek. "Nice meeting you, Nina," I said and smiled. Even though I was troubled by her sudden visit, I couldn't deny she was very nice, polite, and apparently liked me long before I even learned about her existence.

"Hi, Richard," Nina said, giving him a hug. "Here's your paperwork." She handed him a fat folder with files. "You want to go over this?" she asked him. "And by the way, I'm so sorry I interrupted your lunch, guys," she said to me, noticing my unpleasant facial expressions. "That's OK," Richard said, looking through the files. "Yes! It is not a big deal," I said with the same fake smile. "I have to go get ready for a party, and you guys have fun!" I grabbed my car keys and my phone and walked out of the apartment. In the corridor, I waited a minute for Richard to stop me, but it never followed, so, pissed off and offended, I simply left.

Chloe and I met as planned at 6:30 p.m. and drove in my car to this fancy new restaurant in Beverly Hills, where my office Christmas party was hosted. They rented the whole place and even hired a DJ. The party was beautiful. I met some new interesting people and a couple of men even tried to flirt with me, but I couldn't stop thinking about Richard and his so-called friend I had left alone in his apartment. I thought about them at dinner, and then while dancing, and then during the lottery my boss forced us to play. Eventually my obsession took over, and at 10:00 p.m. I apologized to everyone, made an excuse to leave, got in the car, and drove to Richard's place.

After a fifteen-minute drive, I finally made it to Richard's door. I opened it with the key he gave me when we got back together again. "Richard?" I walked into the dark room; the apartment was empty. 'What are you up to?' I texted him. 'At dinner with Nina, heading home soon,' he texted back immediately. I poured myself a glass of Sauvignon Blanc, turned on the TV, and sat on a couch waiting for Richard and an explanation. One hour later, I heard giggling in the corridor, and then the door opened, and he and Nina came in.

"Hi!" Richard said, excited when he saw me sitting on his couch. "Hey," said Nina. I was surprised to see her. "You guys went for dinner?" I asked, looking at her. "Yes, and I left some of my stuff, so I came over to get it," she explained. "Hm." I smiled at her, but to my confusion, she wasn't about to leave. Instead, she sat down on the couch next to me and continued talking. "I was bothering Richard with boys talk." She looked at him, and they both chuckled. "I'm sorry?" I said, being the only one in the room who had no idea what was going on. "I was seeking his advice on what to do with my boyfriend," she clarified. "Oh, you have a boyfriend?" She nodded. "We have a lot of problems lately between us," Nina elaborated. "Interesting," I said, sipping my wine, "perhaps the reason you have problems is that at 11:30 p.m. you are not with your boyfriend but with mine," I said to her with a sarcastic smile. Nina didn't say anything back, only smiled, and then ten minutes later, she made an excuse and left.

"Did you have to say that?" Richard asked me, closing the door after his friend. "Say what?" I acted as if I had no idea what he was referring to. "You were mean to her, and she doesn't deserve it," he said. "Chloe doesn't deserve the treatment you are giving her either," I snapped at him, "so don't you lecture me here!" I grabbed my glass and walked to the kitchen to put it in the dishwasher. "What were you two doing all day?" I asked him. "We were working and then I took her to dinner to talk and catch up." "Dinner, huh? And where did you go to have dinner?" "The sushi place at the corner, the one we always go to." He sounded very calm and it seemed didn't mind my questions at all. "She is just my friend. I have known her for one hundred years," he said, coming closer and hugging me from behind. "By the way, you look very beautiful tonight." I looked down. I was still wearing the dress that I got for the Christmas party. "Are you jealous?" Richard asked me, giggling. "Of you?" I looked at his arrogant smile. "NEVER." I rolled my eyes at him, unable to hide a smile.

By the end of December, I had already made Richard watch every holiday-related movie there was. We went to get a Christmas tree. He didn't want it at his place, so we put it at mine instead, and he agreed that on Christmas Eve we would have dinner at my place, have traditional Christmas morning with egg-nog and the unwrapping of presents, and then, after all that, we would go to his friend's house for a party.

"Do we really have to go there?" Richard said as we were choosing a present. "They are your friends. If you don't want to go, you tell them yourself," I said, looking at a vase. "This is beautiful," I said, showing it to Richard. "How much?" he asked without even looking. "Seven hundred, but it's gorgeous." "OK, let's pay for it and get out of here. You know I hate all this Christmas shopping." While looking for the right credit card in his wallet, Richard gave me his phone. "Could you hold it for a sec, please," he asked, handing it over. Suddenly the screen lit up, and I saw a text on IG from some girl asking how his day was. My first instinct was to start a fight, but I controlled myself and decided not to judge right away; after all, she could be his relative or a friend.

On our way home I didn't utter a word. I couldn't stop thinking about who that girl was. "Everything OK?" Richard asked when we were in elevator. "You "you are unusually quiet." "Just in my thoughts, that's all." I tried to force a smile. "What do you want for lunch?" I asked him, walking into the apartment. "I don't know, Thai food?" "OK, let me change, and I'll think about how I feel about Thai." I walked into the closet, opened the drawer where I had all of my home clothes and PJ's stored, and right on top of my stuff, I saw a white T-shirt, which wasn't mine. Immediately I grabbed it and made my way back into the living room like a tornado makes its way through a Midwestern state. "What is this?!" I yelled, throwing the T-shirt at Richard. "A T-shirt," he said, confused. "Oh, really? A T-shirt. Right, thank you, I couldn't remember the name of this thing. Thank you, honey!"

"What?" he said, staring at me.

"Who's T-shirt is it?"

"Yours, probably. Who else?"

"Oh yeah, that would be very logical if my T-shirt were in my drawer, but the problem is it's NOT mine."

"Well then, I don't know, the maid must have put it there."

"I don't care who put it there. If it's not mine, then whose? You are cheating on me, aren't you?"

For a second I paused, waiting for his reaction, but he didn't say anything. "Admit it!" I yelled. "T-shirts, texts from some whore . . ."

"You went through my phone?!" he said furiously. I looked him in the eyes, unable to force out a single word. "Who do you think you are? To go through my phone, read my texts, control me all the time! You are not my wife!" Then he stopped. For a moment, we were just staring at each other speechless. "Give me a bag!" I said, but he didn't move from where he was standing. "Give me a bag!" I screamed hysterically. "What do you need a bag for?" I didn't answer. Instead, I went to the kitchen, got an old shopping bag, and then rushed to the closet. "What are you doing?" Richard followed me. "Making room for your bitches!" I screamed at him while putting all of my clothes into the shopping bag. "This drawer is too small for all of us!"

When I was done with the closet, I went to do the same in the bathroom, and when there was no more evidence of me ever having been in Richard's place, and I was about to order an Uber, I found my phone was dead. "Get me a car!" I commanded Richard, "I want to leave. Now." He obediently ordered an Uber without arguing. "White Toyota Prius in three minutes," he said, showing me the screen. I took all of my possessions and, without saying anything, left the apartment, slamming the door behind me so hard that even the walls shook. I was already halfway to the elevator when I heard the door opening and then

Richard's voice, yelling, "Don't you dare slam doors at me! Bitch." I didn't answer and just kept on walking.

At home, I got drunk. It was the twenty-second of December, and I couldn't have imagined a more miserable way to spend Christmas. I had rejected all invitations thinking I would be with Richard, and now I was alone with no place to spend Christmas.

I spent Christmas Eve with two bottles of wine, and *It's a Wonderful Life* on repeat, even though my life was anything but wonderful at the moment. For Christmas day, Chloe invited me to come to her family's lunch. Hungover and exhausted from the three previous nights of heavy drinking and little sleep, I went to Beverly Center to get a last-minute gift for Chloe's mom, and on my way there, I decided to drop off Richard's gift at his lobby. After all, it was Christmas, a time for miracles. I gave the concierge the apartment number but asked him not to call until after I was gone.

An hour later, I got a text, 'Merry Christmas! Thank you for the gift.'

We didn't talk after that, but then on New Year's Eve, he texted me again. Too bad I was already wasted and blacked out at Highlight Room with my friends. Even though I don't remember almost anything from that night, I have learned some valuable life lessons. Number one, don't mix cocaine and ecstasy, nothing good will come out of it; number two, if you happened to mix them, go home.

XVI

9 CIRCLES

It had been three weeks since Richard and I had our last fight. I wasn't mad at him anymore, but I didn't want to go through all that again. I couldn't know for sure if he cheated on me or not, but I knew that if we were ever to get back together, I would never trust him like I used to. In the past week, Richard made some attempts to get me to speak to him. And then, just before Valentine's Day, he called. "Hi," I said, picking up. "How are you?" he asked, and before I answered, he continued, "I wasn't sure you would pick up." "Neither was I," I said honestly. "The last month hasn't been exactly easy on me," I admitted.

"I know, but I thought maybe we could sit down and talk?"

"I don't know." I wasn't sure it was something I really wanted or something I was ready to do. "Don't answer right away," Richard said, most likely feeling he was being rejected. "It's Valentine's Day on Thursday. Let's have dinner." I chuckled when he said that. "Since when do you care for V-Day?" I teased him. "I don't, but you do, and I wouldn't mind going out with you . . . if it is something you would like,"

"I promise to think about it." "Deal," he said, and I smiled. "Deal."

On Thursday, when I got to the office, a huge bouquet of red roses was waiting on my desk. I felt it was the right thing to text Richard and thank him for the flowers, and if I wasn't sure before if I should go out with him that night, now my mind was made up. The four-hundred-dollar bouquet helped my decision. I left work earlier to get ready for the evening. Richard made a reservation at Il Cielo at 7:30 p.m. and was going to pick me up from my place at 7:00 p.m. Red dress on, Louboutins, full makeup—then at 7:15, he texted, 'Outside.'

The first thing that night that turned me off was the fact that he didn't say a word about the outfit I had put together for him. He picked me up late and now we were late for the reservation. The hostess had given away our table, and we had to wait for the next one at the bar. "Great!" Richard said, trying to make his way through the crowd. "We wouldn't have to wait for a table if we had been on time," I said, irritated.

That night went completely in the wrong direction. We ended up fighting over something so stupid that I don't even remember what it was. In fact, we left the restaurant so mad at each other that he didn't even want to be in the same car with me. Instead, he just got me an Uber, and we called it a night.

After that night, neither Richard nor I made any contact. It was absolutely exhausting to keep up with all that endless drama, fights, scandals, tears, breakups. I wanted a new start, I wanted a renaissance. But life had different plans, and it wasn't going to go easy on me.

At the end of February, I lost my job. Although I'd always hated that place, it was a disastrous turn of events. I've never been great with finances; I didn't have any savings, was spending everything on nights out and clothes, and was left with enormous credit card bills and no income. It was, a time to change the extravagant lifestyle that I couldn't afford, but instead, I told myself I would have a new job in no time, and in the meantime, I could keep living off my credit cards.

With all the free time I had on my hands and the fact I was single again, I decided to get a dating app. It was fun and it boosted my confidence every time a hot guy swiped right on me. I had three dates coming up, plus a group of girls from my previous job invited me to a club on Saturday night. Life started to look brighter, and then when I least expected, I got a text from Kai, and it began to shine. 'I miss you,' he texted me. It was feeding my ego, but I had given myself my word that I would never sleep with him again, and I was going to be true to it. But the more I rejected him, the more he pressured me into meeting, and it was just a question of time before I gave in. I couldn't help but compare Richard to him again, how different they were. Richard was so difficult to deal with when Kai was the definition of easygoing. With Kai, I always had fun. He brought laughter and joy into my life, and he always appeared at my darkest moments. Maybe the universe was trying to tell me something.

On Saturday, I went out to Doheny Room, and after the third cocktail, it struck me: the world had so much to offer and I locked myself up. I'd chosen to be faithful to one person who most likely hadn't done the same, and if he did whatever the hell he wanted in a relationship with me, I surely could do whatever the hell I wanted now! I went outside, picked up my phone, and called Kai. "Hey," he said, picking up on the first ring, "Hi, you!" I sounded drunk.

"What's up?"

"Not much. I'm outside the club and decided it was a perfect time to give you a call." I giggled. "Well, you are always a wanted call." "What are you up to?" I asked him. "Just got back from dinner." He stopped, and I wanted to ask him to meet, but he probably read my mind and said, "Do you want to come over here?" I bit my lip. "You want me to come?" "I do want you to come." His voice sounded very sexy, and even if I wanted to, I could never say no. I went upstairs to say bye to the girls, and twenty minutes later, Kai got me an Uber. When I was already in the car, I realized I didn't know where I was going. I knew that Richard sold his place and was staying at Kai's apartment, so where was Kai staying? We were going west, and fifteen minutes later, I knew I was being taken to Bel Air. The car pulled into the driveway, and I saw Kai near the gates. "Hi, love," he said, giving me a hug. "Hey." I hugged him, placing my hands around his neck.

"It's a nice house," I said, walking in through the door into a big, well-lit hall. "Yeah, I'm staying here for now, but it's my brother's place." Hearing that sentence coming out of his mouth made my blood freeze, and then I remembered that Richard had told me about that place a couple of months ago. It was investment purchase. "Richard is going to move here soon, and I'll get my old place back," Kai continued. "I see." It was all I could say. Fucking my ex's brother was one thing, but doing it at his house was a new level of low, and I had just managed to reach it.

"Do you want anything?" Kai asked me, "Am-drink?" He smiled, looking at me. "What?" I asked, smiling. "I missed that face," he said, looking me in the eyes. I didn't utter a word, my answer was a kiss. I had missed him too, more than I had imagined.

The next morning, I woke up exhausted. He had kept me awake till seven in the morning. I got up and was about to go to the bathroom. "Where are you going?" I heard Kai's voice say, and then he grabbed my hand. "I'm gonna take a shower and go home to get some sleep since you didn't let me have any last night," I teased him and tried to break free, but he pulled me closer and pushed me back into bed. "No! you can't leave! I need you right here with me." He started kissing me and at that moment his phone rang. "Shit!" he said, frustrated, "I need to get that." As he picked up his phone, I went to take a shower.

"Have you seen my underwear?" I asked, walking into the bedroom. "I have." I looked up at him and saw that he was holding them in his hand. "I need them back, thanks." I jumped on the bed and tried to get them back. Kai started giggling, and then he looked at me, sighed, and placed his head on my lap. "I like you," he said quietly, "you know that, right?" "I do," I said, playing with his hair. Moments with him were so peaceful, so natural, sometimes I wondered what it would be like to be with him. Maybe he was right for me. I had never had chemistry like that with anyone else, and yet it was not possible for us to be together.

"I gotta go," I said, getting up from bed and putting my dress on. "Yes, it might be a good idea," he said indecisively. "It was Richard who called earlier." He looked at me, waiting for a reaction, but I didn't say anything. "He wants to meet for lunch and is going to come to pick me up in an hour." "Oh," I said, making a small sound, then continued, "I don't think it's a good idea for him to see me here." "But you don't have to go right away," Kai protested, "we can have breakfast together." "That's sweet of you, but I'd rather not risk seeing your brother." I touched his cheek with my hand and then kissed him. He got me an Uber and walked me to the car. "Can I take you to dinner?" he asked, opening the door for me. "Dinner? As a date?" I smiled.

"Yes."

"I'd like that." I got in the car and blew him a kiss. He laughed. "Text me when you get home," he said, and with that, he closed the car door.

Two days later, Kai asked me out. Besides him, I had another three guys I was going on dates with that week, which I, of course, forgot to mention to him. On Monday, I had a date with this guy I met on Bumble. He was nice, good-looking, and very wealthy.

Weirdly enough, he was Richard's neighbor, and even though he didn't know him personally, he had known of him. His name was William, and he wasn't the typical kind of guy for me—very classy, very old school. What he lacked were drive and humor. For me, it has always been hard to find myself around a man without those qualities. But I took my chances with him—who knew, maybe with time he could win me over.

Two other dates were not even worth talking about. Before the dinner was over, I knew I would block them as soon as I got home. It was the fourth date I looked forward to the most. I was seeing Kai on Friday night. Despite our plan to meet at the restaurant, he texted me at 5:00 p.m., asking if I could be ready in twenty minutes. It was spontaneous, and it was exciting, just like him.

"Where are we going?" I asked, getting in his car. "To dinner," he said and smiled. "Where? You told me to dress comfortably." I was confused. "You'll see." He couldn't stop smiling. "Tell me." I couldn't bear the intrigue any longer, but it seemed he enjoyed teasing me. "Patience is a virtue," he mocked and kissed my cheek.

Once I saw a picnic photo from the beach on Instagram. It was a first date a guy had organized for his crush, and it was absolutely beautiful. No one had ever done anything slightly romantic for me, and I mentioned it once to Kai over a year ago, and now we were on the Pacific Highway going west.

"Gotta make a quick stop," he said, pulling over at In-N-Out drive-through. "Burgers and French fries?" I chuckled. "That's your idea of a romantic dinner date?" He smiled. "I might surprise you, kid." I chuckled one more time.

He took me to El Matador beach, and maybe it wasn't the best date the world has ever seen, but for me, it was for sure the most romantic one. He got a bottle of Dom Pérignon with fast food. His name was written all over it. It was a crazy but amazing combination, just like everything in Kai.

"I have to admit," I started, sipping champagne from a plastic cup, "it's not what comes to a girl's mind when someone invites her on a date, but it's nice." I smiled at him. "Thank you," I whispered. He moved closer and kissed me.

We watched the sunset, we talked, walked on the beach, we ate burgers and drank champagne, and then he drove me back home, walked me to my door, and kissed me good night. It was a perfect date, and walking into my bedroom, I realized it was our first date. Before that, we had sex, we went out to get food, but we had never been on a real date. The thought of it made me smile. I picked up the phone to text Kai, but instead, I had an unexpected surprise. 'Hi Sophie, how are you? I just wanted to say that I'm sorry, I was over the line, and I hope we can talk it out.' "Shit!" I said out loud, he's got to be kidding me.

For the next couple of days, I had insomnia. My options were obvious: first, I could choose Kai, and his newly developed attitude, complete with romantic beach dates, but who knew how long it was gonna last, which led me to choice number two; I could choose Richard and just go back to the way things were, which was sitting at home with take-outs and watching TV nonstop. Or I had the third option, to not give a fuck and do what guys do—hang out with both of them and have a couple of side chicks just in case. Since I couldn't decide, I went with number three . . . at least for the time being.

On Sunday, I went out to brunch with Richard. He wasn't very good at saying sorry, and taking me out to eat was his way of apologizing. I stayed with him for two days, and since I knew Richard and Kai weren't close enough to share any personal life updates with each other, I was absolutely calm about the idea of dating them both and not getting caught. In fact, I didn't stop there, I went out with William again, and that time, after I got to know him better, he didn't seem completely boring. He had an interesting life story, and he was smart and very into me.

That continued for three weeks. I was driving around town from Kai's apartment where Richard was staying to Richard's house where Kai was staying, plus going on occasional dates with William to a golf club, polo matches, and then spending Sundays at Soho House. It was fun. I stopped worrying about things and started living my life.

"Can we meet up today?" Kai asked me over the phone. "I wanted to talk to you about something." "Can we do it over the phone?" I said, "I'm meeting Chloe in an hour."

"I guess we can talk on the phone then." He sounded weird, and I didn't know the reason for that. "Look, we've known each other for what, two years now? I obviously like you, and we have so much fun together." He stopped for a moment. "Yes?" I said, trying to figure out where he was going with that. "What I'm trying to say here is that I want something more than what we have right now . . . I want a relationship." "You mean, you and me?" I asked him, caught completely off guard. "Yes, I just want to try and see how it goes." I didn't know what to say. I wasn't even sure I wanted to have a relationship. To say yes to Kai meant to say farewell to Richard. If there was any chance for us getting back together after I hooked up with his brother, there undoubtedly was zero chance if we were dating. "I can't give you an answer right now," I spilled out, "but I promise to think about it," I said, trying to make my rejection sound a little better. "Yeah, OK." "I've got to go get ready, but I'll talk to you later," I said, making some weird nervous sounds.

Chloe and I went to Beverly Hills for dinner, and around midnight we ended up standing in a huge line to get into some club in Hollywood. "Should we just go somewhere else? We never wait in a line," Chloe said, shifting from one foot to the other. "No! It's a matter of principle now. We have been waiting for fifteen minutes. I'm not going anywhere!" I protested. Another fifteen minutes, and we were finally inside. The club was full. We decided to walk around in case we met someone we knew and luckily this someone had a table. We circled once around the club. Nothing. Twice. Nothing again. And then . . . "It's Kai! Look, at the table next to the DJ!" Chloe almost screamed, pointing with her head in his direction. There he was, waving at me and smiling. We made our way through the crowd to the table "Hey, Fifi," Kai said, giving me a kiss on the cheek. "Hey, Chlo," he said, hugging Chloe. "What do you guys wanna drink?" he asked, calling a waitress over. "I'll do martini, thanks," I said. "I'll do margarita," I heard Chloe say. "So, who are you here with?" I asked Kai. "Here, these are my good friends," he called out to one of the men at the table, introducing us. "This is Sophie." I smiled at the guy. "Nice to meet you." "It's very nice to meet you, Sophie. I'm Nick." "And that's Chloe," Kai continued. "These two are crazy, you'll love them." "Excuse me," Kai said when his phone rang, then he walked away, leaving us at a table full of strangers. For the first five minutes, we talked to that Nick guy, but he left us as well, turning to the group of girls at the next table. "Maybe we should just go to the bar," I said to Chloe. "Why?" "Kai is acting weird. Let's just go, please." "Fine, let's go, I don't mind." And just as we were trying to leave, Kai got back. "Where are you going?" he asked Chloe. "We are going to the bar!" I answered for her. "Why? Stay here," he said, confused. "Thanks, but we'll go hang there."

"What was all that about?" Chloe asked me at the bar as we waited for our drinks. I looked at her, not knowing if I should tell the truth, and after a moment of hesitation, I spilled, "He called me today, asking to meet. I was getting ready for dinner and told him I couldn't, so long story short, he asked to start dating." "And that's bad why exactly?" She looked at me, lifting an eyebrow. "Think about it!" I argued. "I date him, everyone is gonna find out, and people already know I dated Richard, so how is it going to make me look?" "It sure as hell doesn't bother him, so why does it bother you? I think there is a different reason," Chloe said. "Which is?" I asked, perfectly well aware which reason she meant; the name of that reason was Richard. "I will think about it, and you are wrong, there is no other reason," I lied to her. "Fine!" she said, "but if I were you, I would give it some serious thought."

At the bar, we met some weird guys who paid for our drinks, and then we talked to them for the next thirty minutes at their table. It was better than staying in the middle of the club with all this crowd. I was pretending to listen when I noticed an interesting scene happening just four feet from our new table. It was Kai and some blondie giggling. "Look at this!" I said to Chloe, knocking her with my elbow. "Shit," she said when we noticed that they started kissing. Without any hesitation, I placed my glass on the table and walked straight up to him. He was still busy, caught up in the process, so I placed my hand on his shoulder to make my presence known. "Thank you," I said sarcastically, "you made the choice easy for me," and then I smiled, looked him in the eyes, and walked away. "Sophie! Sophie, wait!" I heard him saying, but I didn't even look back.

Not only did I sleep like a baby that night, but the next morning I knew exactly what I wanted. I picked up my phone and called Richard. Three calls and still no answer, and then I got a text. 'Don't bother! I've heard.'

XVII

IT'S A RICH MAN'S WORLD

A couple of months in, thousands in debt, bills past due, and no job. For some, that would be a troubling time, to say at least. For me, it was double troubling. Almost a month had passed, and Richard still wasn't talking to me, and I was still not talking to Kai.

I was now dating William. He was a nice, caring guy, very romantic, emotionally mature, and, unlike many in LA, he wanted a relationship. Any woman would be satisfied to have a man like him by her side, any woman, but not me, that is. I couldn't help but feel that something or someone was missing. It was then and there I realized that two years of constant drama with Richard and Kai not only wasn't unpleasant to me but that I loved it. I hadn't even noticed that it had become an inseparable part of me, and I couldn't live without all that action, without drama, fights, suspicion, hiding. I had become a junkie, and those two brothers were my heroin. For two years I had told myself how much I wanted for all of it to stop, how much I was done with them, but in the end, it was nothing but a lie, first of all to myself. I wasn't done with them because I didn't want to be. The sick game the three of us were playing had now become my life.

"Do you think we might see him tonight?" I asked Chloe as we got ready for a night on the town. "Who?" she asked, trying on a new dress we'd bought earlier that afternoon. "Kai," I said, opening the second bottle of wine. "You think we might meet him tonight?" "I thought you didn't want to meet him, no?" She was confused. In fact, so was I. For almost a month, I had ignored all his attempts to talk to me. I was still mad from that scene in the club, and now when he stopped texting and calling, I got even madder. "I don't know," I said, unsure of myself, "maybe I'm ready to forgive him." I looked at her, waiting for a reaction, but before she said anything, I corrected myself. "Probably I'm just bored with Will and looking for something to spice it up." "Huh?" Chloe mumbled. "Jesus, are you even listening. I'm busting my ass here to get some advice," I said, annoyed. "What advice do you want? You'll do everything your own way in the end. What's the point of my advice?" I knew she was right, but it was not in my nature to agree that easily. "You know, as my best friend, you are criminally ill-informed about what's going on in my life," I said, trying not to laugh. "Jesus fucking Christ, Sophie." We started giggling together. "What do you need Kai for?" I raised my eyebrow. "Really?"

I chuckled, "I mean, you are dating now." I couldn't stop laughing. "Stop it," Chloe said, throwing a little cushion at me, "I'm dating, yes." I got serious for a second. "But he is this Mr. Perfect, with his perfect apartment, perfect job, perfect manners, perfect life, and I'm not perfect, and I love that about myself." I stopped, taking a breath, and then continued,. "You know that he makes me eat breakfast with a napkin on my lap and fork and knife in my hands. It's too much for me." "The sex isn't good, huh?" Chloe asked straight to my face. "Is that the real reason?" She chuckled. "It's not bad, but he is no Kai, for sure," I admitted, and we started laughing.

That Friday night, despite all my efforts, I didn't met Kai. I didn't meet him on Saturday either, even though I made Chloe stop by the clubs where he would normally hang out. I was so upset, and yet my pride would never allow me to text him first, not after he kissed some blond bitch that night. Losing all my hopes of seeing him that weekend, I decided that Sunday I would spend in bed eating junk food and watching Netflix, and just when I started to execute my plan, my phone beeped. First I thought it was a text from Chloe, who was trying to make me go to some stupid daytime party, so I didn't even bother checking my phone, but then I got another beep and another one. Those texts turned out to be the highlight of my day—the sender was none other than Kai. He was inviting me to have lunch together and then go with a group of his friends to that exact party Chloe wanted to drag me to. I was happy to finally hear from him, so naturally, I texted, 'No, thanks for the invite, you should take the blondie though.' The minute I hit send, he called me back. "What is it?" I asked wittily. He was laughing. "Fifi"—he loved to call me that, mainly because it pissed me off—"I thought you would be glad to hear from me."

"You thought wrong!" Obviously, it was a lie, I knew it, and probably he knew it too. "Come on, let's go to lunch and then party." "I already gave you an answer to that." I sounded sassy. "Are you serious?" he asked. "You still mad at me for kissing that girl even though you were the one who dumped me?" "I didn't dump you!" I argued. "I said I would think about getting together, and before I even got a chance, you were already with someone else, so yes, I am still mad." I raised my voice saying that. "Look, I'm sorry, and I hope we can put it behind us and still be friends."

"Friends with benefits," I said in my head, saying "Friends is good" out loud. "I'll pick you up in an hour. How that sound?" he asked me. "OK, I'll go with you, because I don't have anything better to do anyway. But I'm taking Chloe with me, so make sure to bring a friend and not an ugly one." He started laughing. "OK, I'll bring her a date."

We went to Santa Monica for lunch, and I've got to admit, it was the best day I'd had had in weeks. Kai made me laugh nonstop. He has always had that effect on me. After lunch and one too many glasses of sangria, we headed to a day club. Kai introduced Chloe and me to a group of his friends, and everything was going well and pleasant until a girl named Rose said, "Kai, your brother just texted, he might stop by to say hi." I turned to Kai. He had the same worried expression on his face. I walked over to him. "What are we gonna say if he sees us together?" I was very troubled. Just the thought of what might happen if Richard came to that club terrified me. "Nothing." Kai was making an effort to remain calm, but I could see right through him. "I'll talk to him if he comes," he said, "but you should probably delete all our texts, just in case," he continued. "In case of what?" I asked him without a clue what he meant. "In case he somehow gets your phone from you," Kai explained.

In an attempt to prevent any fights that Richard's arrival might cause, Chloe and I went to explore what that day club had to offer. "We'll just pretend we are not with Kai," I said to her as we wandered around. Forty minutes later, and still no sign of Richard. "I don't think he's coming after all," Kai said when Chloe and I finally made it back to the group.

Around 7:00 p.m. the club started to get empty, and Kai's friend offered to move the party to his place. I still wonder how we made it there alive. None of us was in any condition to drive, and yet it did not stop anyone. Thank God the traffic was light, and thirty minutes later, we ended up somewhere in The Valley. The house was gorgeous, even too gorgeous for a single man in his thirties. "You live here by yourself?" I asked, gazing around. "Oh, no, that's my parents' place. I live in a guest house." "Oh," I said simply, not knowing the proper way to react and still be polite. The idea of living with parents to me equaled being a loser, especially in your thirties.

Despite that, the night was going great. Everyone was so friendly to both Chloe and me, and it seemed only Kai had no interest in my company. He was either talking to that Rose girl or smoking outside. Chloe was playing music, and I was dancing with a group of guys when I noticed Kai going outside for another smoke break. I followed him and sneaked out to the backyard. "Hey," he said, noticing me. "Hi," I said, coming closer. "I thought you don't want to talk to me or something," I continued, looking at him very carefully, trying to understand what was going on in that pretty head of his, but he only grabbed my hand, pulling me closer. "No," he finally said, "of course I want to talk to you, always." He kissed me on the cheek. "Is everything OK?" I asked with genuine care. "Now it is," he said, looking at me, but I knew something was bothering him, I just didn't know what it was. "You should get back inside," he said, taking off his jacket and putting it on my shoulders, "it's cold out here." "It's OK, I'll stay with you, and we go together." But he insisted, and I went back to the house.

In the next hour, things got wild. Cocaine was all over the place, everyone was doing lines, giggling, drinking, and dancing, and I was no exception.

I was sitting on a couch talking and arguing with this guy Jim. He seemed to be a nice person with a lot of knowledge and expertise in the same field I was looking for a job in. We clicked, and I truly enjoyed his company, and I guess it showed because out of nowhere, Kai came over to me saying it was time to get ready and go home. "Oh, OK, but let me drive though, you're still a little drunk," I said and was about to say goodbye to Jim when Kai corrected me. "No, I'll get you and Chloe an Uber, and you'll go home." My face flushed. It was unexpected, and I didn't know how to react. "You won't come with us?" I asked to make sure I got everything right, "I'm not going home just yet." He bit his lip and glanced at Rose. I swallowed nervously. "Can I talk to you?" I walked him from the couch to a little bar on the other side of the living room. "Why are you acting this way?" I asked, trying to get any reasonable explanation. He looked at me, then across the room at Jim, and then turned his eyes back to me. "It's late, and it's time to go home," he said with finality, and I noticed some hatred in his look that scared me a little.

Kai got us an Uber. "Thank you so much for having us," I said to the host, whose name I can't even recall now, then I hugged Jim. "It was so great to meet you," I murmured. "It was a pleasure," he said to me, smiling. "Well, you've got my number. I hope we can stay in touch." He nodded, and after a long goodbye, we were finally ready to get going. "You are coming with us?" I asked in surprise, noticing Kai heading toward the door as well. "Yes," he said shortly, "I'll walk you to the car." He opened the door and pointed at it with his eyes. Chloe exited first, I right behind her.

"I can't believe that!" Kai said to me as soon as we were outside. "What?" I asked in confusion. "You are such a slut!" he said accusingly. "Oh, guys, I'll wait in the car," Chloe said to us. "Bye, Kai." He turned to her. "Bye, Chlo, it was great seeing you." He waved at her and then turned his attention back to me. "You came with me and started flirting with every guy in the room," he said in a cold voice. I saw that he was trying to suppress rising anger. "I'm not my brother," he said. "I'm not going to take shit like this from you." My heart was pounding, and for a moment, I couldn't find the right words. When I opened my mouth, he beat me to it. "You have a good night," he said quickly and then turned around, heading back inside.

I couldn't understand what had just happened or what had caused the reaction I'd gotten. I was used to such episodes with Richard but never with Kai. Was I the problem, or was it just running in the family?

As much as I wanted to obsess over that night, the next week brought me another reason to obsess. I received my credit card statements and bills. Three thousand dollars minimum payment on my Amex, eight hundred on my Visa, rent due in a week, and no way out. The real world had finally gotten to me, and I was absolutely unprepared.

Over the next couple of days, I started texting everyone I knew to ask if not for the whole amount, at least for some part of it, but who would have five thousand dollars just lying around waiting for you?! I knew I needed to text men, guys who had crushes on me, or guys who swore they were my close friends. At that point, I wasn't panicking. After all, I had so many acquaintances. Some of them would lend me some money, for sure. Obviously, my closest friends were ready to help me out. The only problem—they were no better with finances than me, or maybe even worse. After three days of asking everyone I knew and getting polite rejections, I started to get worried. I realized most people who pretended to be my friends were just talk. In a time of need, there was no one I could really rely on. The one person I always knew would help me was Richard, but after everything that went down between us, I was sure he wouldn't be an option.

Another couple of days later and all I had was $1,500 that wouldn't even cover my rent, which was due in three days. I started to get really bad anxiety, and after my unsuccessful attempts and disappointment with everyone, I decided I would text Richard and ask for help. After all, what was the harm in trying?

I fully prepared myself mentally for both the inevitable rejection, which would be the best-case scenario, and to be completely ignored, which would be the worst. When I was texting my heart started racing, and it almost felt like it was going to jump out of my chest. I pressed send and began to wait. The wait was unbearable. Every minute felt like an hour. I wasn't able to think of anything but his text, and constantly checked my phone for the next thirty minutes. One hour passed, and still no answer. He won't answer, I thought to myself. And why would he, after everything I did? Then I heard my phone beeping—

It was a text from Richard, and in a second my racing heart stopped and felt so calm, as I hadn't in a very, very long time, 'How much do you need?' his text said, I texted him an amount, and he simply replied, 'OK, no problem, I'll send it to you right now'. I didn't know what to say. Of course, he obviously had money but so did every other guy I texted. Of course, Richard and I had history, but again so did every other guy. And yet Richard was the only one who apparently cared enough.

I got the money transfer in the next fifteen minutes, and there was no limit to my gratitude. I texted Richard, but somehow he wasn't interested in having a conversation with me, and I was confused. He helped me out, but he wasn't looking to see me or even talk to me at that point. I decided I wasn't going to give it too much thought. I could finally stop worrying and go back to living my life, for one more month at least.

The next day William wanted to meet, and although I wasn't that into him, I agreed. He took me out for dinner, and later we ended up at his apartment. We had some wine and then, watched a movie he picked that made me think about Richard, who had always left the choice of a movie to me, no matter how much he hated it. To be absolutely honest, everything that night was reminding me of Richard and made me think about how lucky I was to have him in my life, even if it was not as a boyfriend but only just as a friend. "By the way, how's job searching going?" Will asked me, cleaning up the table. It was one of his perfect habits that were constantly pissing me off. "It's not going, actually," I said. He gazed at me, looking a bit lost. "I couldn't find anything and had to ask friends to lend me some money, but apparently I don't have as many friends as I thought," I clarified. "I ended up asking for money from my ex," I murmured. He glanced at me. "From Richard?" He sounded surprised. I had totally forgotten he knew him. "Yes," I said simply. "Why didn't you ask me?" he asked, gazing at me again. Why hadn't I? I thought to myself, and my face flushed. "I didn't think that would be comfortable," I said, trying to find an excuse. "We don't know each other that well yet."

"I see," he said shortly. We sat in uncomfortable silence for the next couple of minutes. I was trying to figure out what was going on in his head, but how could I, when I had no idea what was going on in my own? I didn't feel like staying at his place, so after the movie, I made some stupid excuse and left.

Thanks to Richard, my life was back to normal, and on Friday a friend from my previous job invited me to her birthday party. The dinner was hosted at a Mexican restaurant. Not being a big fan of that cuisine, I wasn't very happy with the location choice but had no other option but to attend. The dinner was fun, but to my surprise, some of the people wanted to call it a night at 11:00 p.m. A party animal, I couldn't let that happen, and convincing a couple of girls and dragging Chloe from her home, I threw my own little party. I took them to a hookah place in Westwood.

The night was young, and I was drunk and ready to start making calls. "Let's call Kai," I said, giggling to Chloe in a restroom line. "Yeees! Call him!" She sounded excited. Considering that the last time we saw each other, he had called me a slut, it wasn't a good idea to call him, but at the time, it seemed brilliant. So, while we were in a line, I dialed his number and before it even started ringing, my call went straight to voice mail. "What the fuck?" I cursed, hanging up. "He blocked me!" I said furiously. "Try again," Chloe said in frustration, "there is no way he blocked you." It was almost as though she, too, were trying to convince herself of this. I called again, but this time instead of going to voice mail, it rang for a minute without an answer. "What the hell?!" I couldn't hide my frustration. In the two years that we had known each other, it was the first time he had ignored me so blatantly. We got back to the table, but there was no chance I would just let that go. No, instead, I asked for Chloe's phone and started calling him. "What's up?" I heard him saying. "It's Sophie," I said very loudly. "Oh, I know, Fifi!" He sounded very amused. "If you know, then why didn't you answer my phone calls?" I asked straightforwardly. "You don't know, huh?" My mouth dropped open, but I had no idea how to answer him. Of course I knew why he was acting that way. How couldn't I know? He had told me straight to my face. "Are you mad at me?" I asked, playing dumb. "I was," he answered honestly. "I didn't want to talk to you ever again."

"So, what changed?" I asked boldly. "I don't know. It's hard to explain," he said, and I was afraid he was about to start talking about feelings again. "You want to come join us?" I asked to change the subject. "No, I don't feel like going out. I would love to see you, though." "Where?" I asked. "I'm at my friend's if you wanna come here." Without a second thought, I agreed. The plan was to hang with the girls, but for no longer than thirty minutes—since I was the one who dragged them there and it would be beyond rude to just leave, no matter how tempted I was—then go to Kai's friend's house together with Chloe.

An hour later, we were sitting in his friend's living room. I had been there several times before, and, weirdly enough, every time, my night had ended in a fight and me storming out. Maybe that place was cursed or something.

Chloe was half asleep on a couch, and Nate, the owner of the place, was already in his bedroom all the way asleep, so even if I had wanted a fight, there was literally no one there to assist me. I felt relieved. The evening seemed uneventful, completely opposite what I had in mind when I called Kai, and he seemed to be ill-humored that night. We were sitting side by side, not saying anything, when I noticed a scar on his hand I had never seen before. "Where did that come from?" I asked, taking his hand in mine and gazing at it. "I punched a wall once," he said, moving his hand. "A girl was behaving the same way you did, and I got really mad." He looked me straight in the eye, and I flushed. He had caught me off guard, and I had no idea what to say. Without waiting for my reaction, he continued, "If I ever see you with that fucking guy again, I swear to God I will kill him." I had never seen him like that before. His eyes seemed to have turned red with rage. "I was talking to him because he is your friend," I tried to explain, but he wasn't interested in listening. "I already told you once, I'm nothing like my brother. I'm not going to take shit like that from you!" he said, now nearly shouting at me. "Why would you bring this up?" I said, raising my voice and regretting I had asked about that damn scar in the first place. All that yelling at each other woke Chloe up, and Kai immediately made her a part of the discussion. "Chloe knows what I mean," he said, turning to her, "sleeping with my brother after me. How could you?" "Seriously?" I said, disgusted, "you wanna discuss this? Well, let's discuss it then." I was yelling now. "You were the one who started all of this. I dated Richard and had no intentions of ever getting together with you!" I went full defense. "Guys, I don't want to be a part of this. I'm going home," Chloe said, rising from the couch, but neither Kai nor I paid her any attention. "You know what?" Kai said, "I'm happy that you showed your true nature! I wanted to have a relationship with you, convinced by who you pretend to be. You are nothing but a manipulative slut!" "Oh really!? Look who is talking! Fucking your brother's girl and still acting so innocent! You are a hypocrite!" I yelled. "You don't know anything about my relationship with my brother!" Kai said, standing up, and I rushed to stand up as well. "I know everything!" I said, moving closer to him and looking him straight in the eye. "He was my boyfriend, if you remember," I said, trying to shame him. "We shared everything." He laughed sarcastically. "Everything, huh?" I knew exactly what he was implying. "Yes, everything! You think he doesn't know we fucked?" The tension in the room was palpable, and then Kai finally said, "Go to him then." His voice was calm. "I'm not going to fight every person and all of my friends because you are who you are and always act accordingly." He looked at me and added, "If Richard loves it, let him continue to make a fool of himself because I don't want it. You are not worth it!" I looked at him. So coldhearted, so insensitive. He was full of hate—hate for me, for Richard, for that poor guy who did nothing but talk to me. I didn't know this Kai and had never intended to meet him. . . Without saying another word, I walked out . . . again.

That apartment was definitely cursed!

XVIII

A MAN WHO ALWAYS COMES BACK

As I walked home half-drunk, in high heels, at five in the morning, I started to think about my life. What was wrong with me? Was the problem my poor choices in men, or was I the real problem? How often do we just stop and look in the mirror? Do you like what you see there? At that particular moment, I didn't like myself. I didn't like the person I was becoming—unstable, hysterical, dramatic—and yet somehow, it was beyond my ability to prevent it. I started thinking about the men who surrounded me. All of them liked me, all of them talked big, and yet all of them left me when I needed their help. All but one. The one I was hurting the most seemed to be the only one who cared enough. Was it possible I just didn't want to be happy? There was no other explanation. I knew I had loved Richard at some point, and I knew he cared about me, and it seemed we both could never let go of each other, so why did we keep hurting each other? Was there any chance things would change? And if yes, was he willing to take that chance?

Lost in my thoughts, I hadn't even noticed how I made it home. The sun was up. It was a new day, a new start. I picked up my phone and was about to text Richard when I got a message from Chloe instead. It's a sign, I thought to myself, deciding that probably Richard and I were never meant to be. Unless of course, he texted me first, then I might reconsider destiny.

My last date with Will wasn't exactly a success, so it came as no surprise that after two weeks he still hadn't called. But to be absolutely fair, it didn't really upset me. Quite the opposite, actually. But without Kai's company, with William going MIA, and with Richard being totally uninterested in me, I felt a strong need for a change of scenery.

I complained about it to Chloe, and the next day we were on a flight to Miami. If you need a definition of denial, this is exactly the right place to look for it. Broke, without a job or any source of income, in tons of dept, and yet I still went on vacation. Hakuna matata, motherfuckers. During our three days in Florida, we did coke, we did guys, we went to pool parties—we did basically everything except spending a night in our expensive-ass hotel. Actually, we didn't sleep at all at that point. Miami was definitely everything I had expected and everything I hadn't.

That vacation, no matter how irrational, was

the best medicine. For three days, not even once did Richard or his brother appear in my mind, and when I finally stopped thinking about him, he started thinking about me. 'Hi, how have you been?' I read a text from Richard, turning my phone on in LAX. The game was officially back on!

On Thursday, Richard invited me to his new house, the same house in which I'd had sex with his brother two months before. On my way to Bel Air, I gave myself a pep talk, trying to relax and get rid of the anxiety that so inconveniently struck me. He had no idea about Kai and me, and he didn't need to know. It's all in the past, so leave it there, I told myself. I didn't even notice how I made it to the front gate.

"What a beautiful neighborhood," I said as I walked in holding the orchid I had gotten Richard as a housewarming present. "Here, I got it for you," I said smiling, handing him the flower. "Oh, thank you," Richard said, and a soft smile appeared on his face. "Do you want a tour?" he asked me with some childish excitement. I nodded. I had seen every room and every corner of that house, but the tour guide was different back then. Richard walked me around, going on and on about the house. I should have felt horrible, but I didn't. Maybe I felt bored, but not guilty or ashamed. After the tour, Richard announced he was going to cook dinner for me, something he had never done before. Breakfasts, soups when I was sick, yes, but never dinner. He grilled some steaks and chopped up some salad, and let me tell you, it was one of the best meals I have ever had. "I didn't know you could cook like this," I said, enjoying the last bite of my meat. "It was great." I smiled. He was gazing at me with a smirk on his face. "I have a lot of talents," he said, turning his attention from me to the plate. "Yeah, that you do." I smiled again. "How have you been?" he asked. "Good," I said simply, trying not to go into details. "Hmm," he said noncommittally. "And you? How is everything?" "Good," he said shortly. "I'm going to clean up, and you can pick a movie. How's that sound?" he asked, rising from his chair. "Oh la la," I said flirtatiously. "Are you trying to impress me?" I teased. "Delicious dinner, no cleaning up, and I get to choose the movie." I smiled, walking closer to him. "You don't have to try so hard, I am already impressed," I whispered, kissing his cheek. After the three-hour movie I picked ended, we were both exhausted and headed to bed. He opened the bedroom door, and I walked in—thank God it was not the same one I'd occupied during my last visit.

"I have to go to the office," Richard said in the morning, making coffee. "Do you want to stay here or come with?" "You mean to the office?" I asked, surprised. He had never invited me to see his workplace before. "Yes, to the office . . . if you want," he said, pouring coffee into a cup. "Yes!" I sounded joyful. "I'd love to come with you." It was official, we were back together once again.

When we got to his work, everyone instantly knew who I was. I was the boss's girlfriend, and I'm not gonna lie, it felt pretty good. The secretary was offering me drinks, coffee, snacks, everyone was trying to make me like them, and I absolutely enjoyed that ass-kissing atmosphere. "How come you never invited me to come here before?" I asked, walking into his office. He looked at me. I knew he was amused by this question. "I have a meeting, but it shouldn't be too long, maybe an hour tops. You can stay here or just wander around. If you need anything, just ask the secretary. Her name is Jenny." I was impressed. He seemed so different, so professional, and so hot. "If you get bored, you can use my computer," he said, waving at a laptop on his desk. "Don't worry, I will find a way to entertain myself." I smiled, flopping down into his chair.

As promised, he finished his meeting in one hour, during which I did nothing but watched some silly YouTube videos. "Are you ready to go?" Richard asked, walking in. "Go?" I was surprised. It was barely past 11:00 a.m. "Yes, let's go." He grabbed a folder full of documents from his desk and pointed me toward the door. "Let's go," he said one more time. "I thought you had to be in the office today," I asked in confusion as we waited for an elevator. "That's a perk of being the boss." He smiled with some pride. "Where are we going now?" I murmured, walking into the elevator and pressing the lobby button. "I have to drop off this paperwork at my friend's house, and then we can go have lunch. What do you want to eat?" "I don't know. Sushi?" I asked, unsure. "OK, we'll go to a sushi place then." It was as if Richard had been replaced by an identical twin who had a better character. He was a different person—agreeable, polite, considerate. All of it felt off. "What's going on with you?" I asked him suspiciously. "What do you mean?" "I mean, you don't seem yourself." "Huh?" he asked, confused. "Dinner, cleaning up—you hate cleaning up—and being so nice and agreeable." I looked at him, demanding an explanation. "I want to give it a second chance," he said, looking at me, "to see how things might go between us. I don't want to screw it up again." I was touched. "Yes," I said quietly, "I'd love that too, the second chance." He smiled at me kindly.

We were spending twenty-four-seven together, and not even once did we argue or yell or curse at each other. It started to seem that after all there was indeed a second chance, or more like a fifth, in our case. Richard wanted to be with me every second of every day, and I didn't know what changed, but something did change completely. Because despite his desire to be with me every second of every day, he was OK with me going out, "as long as you come back to my place to spend the night," as he put it, and I couldn't argue with that. Since I was still on the market for a job, I was going with him to his office. He put a second desk next to his own. It was now my workstation. I loved it, loved the way I was treated by him, by his employees, by his friends, and loved my new routine, even though it was revolving around a man.

Richard introduced me to some of his married friends and their families, and now instead of partying at daytime clubs, I was having lunches and tea parties with a bunch of married couples, and, as surprising as it might seem, I enjoyed that change. The only part that was making me uncomfortable was the questions from his friends about when we were going to get married or have kids. It was too early for those kinds of questions, although deep inside, I liked to imagine that one day we might indeed get married, move in together, have children, have a family. But just then, what we had was enough for me.

It had been more than two months since I had last slept in my own bed. Richard took me anywhere and everywhere with him—business meetings, dinners with colleagues, dinners with friends, shopping with his mom, everywhere. And after a day of this and many other activities together, we would end up at his place, which now seemed to be my permanent residence. But as much as I loved this, I missed my apartment. What was the point of paying rent, which Richard now covered, and using the place? After a long discussion, he compromised. We would spend at least two days a week at my home. On Friday morning, I helped Richard pack some of his clothes for the fun weekend at Sophie's. Everything was great. We spent the afternoon eating ice cream and riding Bird scooters in Santa Monica, hit the movies in the evening, and were home in time for dinner. That night we ordered pizza and finally got a chance to catch up on the last *Game of Thrones* episode. A perfect Friday.

"I have some stuff to do today," Richard said

to me as I was making breakfast. "Yes?" I asked casually. "What kind of stuff?" "Just something." It felt off, so I asked again, "Something like what?" I was persistent. "I'm gonna go to the chiropractor," he said, checking his phone. "On a Saturday?" I wasn't going to let it go. Something about it didn't feel right, and I was determined to get to the bottom of it. "Yes, on a Saturday," he repeated, avoiding my gaze. "Fine, where is this chiropractor?" I asked, gazing at him and trying to catch his reaction. "Hm, it's somewhere in West Hollywood, very close to your place," he said quickly. "OK, I'll come with and hang at Beverly Center while you're there." "You don't have to come," he said, glancing at me. "Why not? I don't mind." He was lying, and I could feel it from ten miles away. "Why do you have to start fighting me?" Richard jumped to offense. "Oh, I'm not the one looking for trouble here, you are!" "I'm sorry?" he asked, turning his attention from the phone to me. "You are being weird, and you are lying to me! There is no chiropractor!" I said straightforwardly. He looked at me and said, "You want me to call him and put it on speaker for you? Why do I have to explain myself?" "It doesn't make sense!" I said. "You always ask me to come everywhere with you, and now suddenly you don't even want me to know where you are going?" "Exactly!" he said, raising his voice. "We are always together! Why is it so hard for you to imagine that I might need some alone time?" "I . . . hmmm," I murmured. "I didn't say anything, to avoid this," he explained, and yes, maybe it did make sense, but something still felt off to me. "Fine, go to your chiropractor," I said, picking up a plate and walking to the living room. He followed me. "You don't have to be suspicious of me every time!" he said, annoyed. "If I say I'm going to the doctor, then I'm going to the doctor." "OK," I said simply. I wanted to believe him, and even though my gut was telling me the opposite, I decided to cut him some slack. "If you say so, I believe you. I'm not suspicious," I said, trying to force a smile. After breakfast, he took a shower and left to see a "chiropractor," and as much as I hate to admit it, I did enjoy that little bit of alone time. Even though I spent it doing my laundry and cleaning the house, it still felt nice not to have someone breathing down my neck every second.

Three hours later, Richard still hadn't come home, nor had he called to check in. There is no chiropractor, I thought to myself. In order to ease my mind, I decided to go grocery shopping. Walking down the aisle, I started to think, when was it that my life began revolving around a man? Absolutely everything I was doing and thinking was somehow always linked to Richard. I had become one of those "we" women I so much despised some time not so long ago. Richard was bringing out the housewife in me, and I had mixed emotions about whether or not I liked this version of myself or not.

When I got home, he was still not there. I couldn't bear it much longer, so I called. But he canceled my call and texted me instead, saying that he was driving home. That had a fishy smell all over it. I knew I promised myself not to start a scandal and not to accuse him of anything, but I just couldn't help myself. I felt that he was lying, and I didn't know how or why. I just felt it.

"Hi," he said, walking in. He seemed to be in a very good mood, and I was determined to change that. "So, how was your chiropractor?" I asked, staring at the TV.

"I didn't go there," he said, taking off his shoes.

"No?" I asked, surprised. "Then where have you been for the past four hours?"

"I met with Sam, and then I went to have lunch and some ice cream," he said as if he were my employee making a report, "and I brought you some ice cream as well." "You went to lunch alone?" I asked suspiciously. "Yes, Sam had a meeting." His voice sounded very calm. "OK," I said in the same calm manner. Maybe I was making too much of a deal out of it after all. I decided to let it go. "What kind of ice cream?" I asked, grabbing the bag from his hands. "Vanilla," he said, going to the kitchen. As I started to unpack the bag, a check fell from it and landed on my lap. I'm not sure how many people know it, but restaurants have this cool thing where on top of the check, they indicate the number of people that were dining with them. I, for one, knew it very well, and Richard's check was clear as day, unlike its owner. "Who did you go with?" I asked without hesitation. "Go where?" he said, pretending he didn't understand. "Don't play dumb with me!" I grabbed the bag and walked to the kitchen counter. "Here!" I said, lifting the check to his face. "Here's what? My receipt for the ice cream from the restaurant." "Yeah, I can read." I was getting angry. Did he really think I was stupid enough not to notice that there were two of them in the restaurant? "I'll ask again, who you were with?" I sounded demanding, possessive even. "I told you already. I was alone!" he said, annoyed. "Then why does it say, two people?" I yelled at him, pointing at a check. "What?" Richard asked, confused, "I don't know why it says it. I told you I was alone. Why are you acting like this?" "Like what?" He looked at me, hesitating, and then spelled it out. "Like a crazy person." "You are seeing someone else!" I drew a conclusion. "I knew it!" I yelled, turning around and heading toward the bedroom. "Where are you going?" he asked, following me. "Just admit it!" I said, turning to him. "It's not exclusive, and you are seeing other people!" But he wasn't saying a word, only looking, and I noticed a ghost of a smile on his face. He was actually enjoying this scene. "Look," he finally said, "I'm not seeing other people. I'm not interested in seeing other people." He smiled. "You will be the first one to know if I have a change of heart, but right now, I don't need anyone else." It was a touching sentiment, and it worked on me. I leaned into him. "If I tell you I was alone, maybe for once you can try and give me at least the benefit of the doubt?" he teased me. "I'll try but can't promise," I said childishly.

Later that evening, there was a birthday party

I had been invited to, and although I asked Richard to come, he preferred to stay in, assuring me he was totally fine with me going. The party was fun, but I decided not to gamble my good fortune with Richard and got home around 1:00 a.m., which made him extremely happy.

"See, you don't even want to party anymore," he said when we were going to bed. "Yeah," I said noncommittally. In reality, I still liked partying, still liked flirting, liked getting drunk, but I was willing to give it up for a chance at a normal relationship with him. "Do you want to go on a hike tomorrow?" I asked him, changing the subject and getting under the sheets. "We'll see," he said, turning off the light, and I chuckled. After almost two years of knowing him, I had a pretty good idea that the answer meant no. "OK, good night," I said, turning to the left side. "Good night," he said, spooning me and kissing my neck.

On our usual Sunday, we would do lunch with Richard's friends, or go to a beach, or to the movies, but that Sunday, he made me go shopping with him. "What exactly are we looking for?" I asked him, exhausted, standing in the fourth sports store we'd been to. "Nothing specific." We had spent three hours and still gotten nothing, and now we were in the Beverly Center, and I had absolutely no idea why. I was simply a follower. "Oh my God!" I screamed in excitement, seeing the most beautiful Prada shoes on display. "Uh-uh, no!" Richard said, noticing my reaction. "I want to try those shoes!" I said, moving toward the entrance. "You don't need another pair of shoes." It was a bad start. "You already have too many." When you thought it couldn't get any worse— and I'm not gonna try to recreate the scene I made as I pleaded with him for the next ten minutes —let's just say I ended up with those shoes, and he ended up with a $1,200 charge on his AmEx.

"OK, let's go check out another store now," he said as we came out of the Prada boutique. At that point, I didn't mind anymore. My mood was significantly improved by the purchase we'd made there. In the next store, when asked by a shopping assistant what he was looking for, Richard gave some confusing answer, and only after five minutes of wandering around did he finally reveal his true intentions. "Do you have skiing costumes?" My eyebrow involuntarily lifted on its own. Skiing costumes? Who goes skiing in eighty-five-degree weather? Where was he gonna go skiing? And if he was planning a skiing trip, why was he trying to hide it from me? Unless he was going with another woman, which, as he had sworn twenty-four hours earlier, was impossible. "Why do you need a skiing costume?" I asked. "You going to ski?" That made the shopping consultant very uncomfortable, and I could feel it, but the thought that my so-called boyfriend was fucking other women was even more disturbing and uncomfortable. "We do not have any skiing costumes left," I heard the assistant say, "but you can check out the store on the Westside." "Will do, thank you!" Richard said, and without saying anything else, headed out of the store.

I followed him in silence. "Why do you need a costume?" I pressured him again. "For the future," he said shortly, getting in the car. "For the future? What future?" I got in the car yelling at him. "You dragged me to billions of different stores, not telling why. If it was just for future needs and not for a vacation with some bitch, then why hide?"

"Hide?" he replied. "You said it yourself. 'I dragged you with.' Would I do that if I was hiding something?" It did make sense, but not at that moment. "Where are we going?" I asked him. "I need to get to that store on the Westside," he said calmly. I started laughing hysterically.

"For the future, huh?"

"OK, Linda invited me to come on a skiing trip next weekend."

Linda. I hated that girl more than anyone can imagine, and the feeling was mutual. I was introduced to her three times, and every time by a different guy.

She and Richard had been friends for a couple of years by then, but I, and pretty much everyone else except Richard himself, knew she had feelings for him. "Linda??" I paused, waiting for a reaction. "Yes, Linda." He was firm. "So you are going on a trip, and you didn't even think of telling me or maybe inviting me with?" "It's a friends trip!" he said, annoyed. "Don't you think I might need some time with my friends? We are together twenty-four seven." "It was your idea!" I said accusingly, "you were the one who decided to spend more time together." "Yes! Because the last time we got together, you kept complaining that we don't spend enough time together," he yelled back at me. "OK, fine! But when were you gonna tell me, huh? Or were you just gonna leave without even saying anything?" "Of course I would tell you!" He started speeding the car. It was a bad sign. "When? When you were already long gone? You keep doing this to me! What kind of relationship is that? You are afraid of real commitment!" I said in anger, immediately regretting going down that road. Richard looked furious, like a bull on a red flag. "First of all, I am committed enough, and second, I don't know what kind of relationship you think we have, but I am not looking for a wife." I flushed. I wasn't particularly looking for a husband either but would be lying if I said it had never crossed my mind. "I thought, or at least I hoped, we have a relationship in which both partners put each other first! I know I do, but it hurts me to realize that apparently, I hardly make a top twenty important things in your life!" "You are doing it again!" Richard said, pulling into a parking lot. Being in the middle of a fight, I hadn't even noticed how we made it to the Westside. "You are manipulating your way, and you have been doing it since day one. You get what you want. In fact, 'want' is the only word you know, and on top of that, you are nothing but a gold digger! Did you really hope I would marry you?" I turned my face, looking at the window. My eyes were full of tears, and I was desperately trying to hold them in and not give him the satisfaction. He left the car without asking me to come with him, and thank God he didn't. The second he left, I started to cry so hard I thought I was gonna flood his car with my tears. In fifteen minutes, he returned with a bag in his hands. Apparently, he'd found what we had spent five hours looking for. On the way back to my place, neither he nor I uttered a word, and though it lasted only fifteen minutes, it was a very long ride. When we finally got home, he headed straight to the bedroom and started packing his stuff. "What are you doing?" I asked with my voice still shaking from all the crying earlier. "What does it look like I'm doing?" he said aggressively. "Are you seriously going to leave like that?" I asked but got no answer, and after he was done packing, he just slammed the front door and left.

Half an hour later and I was still on the floor of my living room crying, experiencing the worst mental breakdown of my life. Richard made me feel inferior, unworthy of love, unworthy of everything, really. No one before or after has ever made me feel that way. I felt so down, to the point where I started to get suicidal thoughts, looking for an easy way out. It scared me, and I knew I really needed someone to talk to. I got dressed, got in a car, and went to Chloe's place. After a long talk, tears, and hysteria, she managed to cheer me up. We danced, we cried, we finished three bottles of wine, and then I blocked

Richard's number. The therapy was completed, and it was a success.

Afraid of being alone and what it might do to my fragile mental health, I stayed with Chloe for the next two days. She was always kind and caring, and unlike many others, never judged me. But my peace had an expiration date, and it came when two days after our crazy fight, Richard slid into my dm's. 'You blocked me?' I tried not to answer, but after terrorizing me, he started to terrorize my friends. He learned where I was, since apparently he had been waiting for me at my place for two days. 'I just want to talk.' 'Please unblock me.' 'I canceled the ski trip, please unblock.' After a resistance that lasted for a day and a half, I gave in. We met at my place, and he did something unusual. He apologized. "You said very hurtful things," I told him. "I said those things in anger," he argued. "Why did you even listen to me?" "Usually, when people are angry, that's when the truth comes up." I paused. "Do you really see me as just fun and nothing serious?" I brought up the question that tormented me the most. "I'm not looking to get married right now, but do you think I would have been here if I saw you as someone just to have fun with?" he said. I looked at him. "I don't know," I said finally. "You hurt me a lot this time, and calling me a gold digger . . ." He stopped me. "I know! And I never meant it because you are anything but that, and I'm sorry, truly, and I promise it won't happen again." I couldn't know for sure that something like that would not take place in the future, but his reassurance was enough at that time. That night we spent talking, and everything seemed to be back to normal, whatever "normal" was.

We both decided that from then on, we would still spend a lot of time together, just not as much as before. After all, it had become the main cause of our last fight. In the morning, we had breakfast together, and then he went to the office, I went to the gym, and after work, he picked me up to go to his house. On the way, we got some Italian food and a bottle of great red wine. I planned to eat, drink, watch a black-and-white movie, laugh, have sex, and then cuddle and fall asleep, but just like always, life had a plan of its own. "Hi," I heard a voice say as we walked into the house. It was coming from the living room. I turned to Richard first, looking for some sort of explanation in his eyes. "Hey guys," I heard the voice say again, this time much closer to me. I turned my head, and there he was, standing four feet away from me, smiling like a Cheshire cat. Kai.

XIX

A GHOST OF SUMMER PAST

In awkward silence, I walked to the kitchen. I needed time to get my thoughts together. Kai was there. Why was he there? Was it some kind of test? Or did they both just want to get back at me in this way? Unpacking the takeout and placing it on plates, I noticed Richard at the kitchen door. "A heads-up would be nice," I said without turning to him. "Yeah, he's going stay with me for some time," Richard said, coming closer to me. "It's going to be awkward," I whispered, "I wish you'd told me." "It won't be awkward," he disagreed. That's because you don't know the whole story, I thought to myself, and then I said, "OK, if you say so." I had so many questions I wanted to ask, like why would he stay there? If Richard had moved out of Kai's apartment, why didn't he just go there? And did Kai know that I would be coming to Richard's place? And if he did, why didn't he say anything to Richard? And if he didn't know, how awkward it must have been for him as well.

Even though I prepared myself for the worst, despite my expectations, it wasn't awkward. Kai was barely at home, and when he was, he usually hung in the guest bedroom that Richard had picked for him. In two weeks, I hadn't spoken to him once, except for brief hellos and brief goodbyes. All in all, things were going pretty well. Richard and I were together when we wanted, and we were apart when we needed.

"There is a big party," I started to say as we were cooking lunch together. "The one on Saturday?" Richard asked, tasting the pasta sauce he was working so hard on. "Yes, I just got an invite," I said, opening my mouth wide, showing him I wanted a taste too. "Is it good?" I swallowed. It was delicious. "Perfection," I said, smiling. "So what about the party? Wanna come?" I asked, noticing a slight change in his expression. "Can I ask you a favor, and you promise not to get mad?" he asked me carefully. "What kind of favor?" "Don't go to that party." "Richard!" I tried to argue. "Please," he said, looking at me with puppy eyes. "I know we talked about it a dozen times, and I'm OK with you going out, but not to this one." "What's the difference between this one and every other party?" I asked, confused. "I know what kind of crowd is gonna be there," he said, turning his attention back to the sauce. "So you don't trust me. Is that what you are saying?" I said, quick-tempered. "I don't trust those guys because I know them," he explained. "Hey, I have a business dinner on Friday. Why don't you go out with Chloe or some of your girls then?" I knew he hated the idea but was trying to please me, and I appreciated the effort. "OK, I'll go out on Friday. It would be good to catch up with Chloe." When Friday came, I did exactly that. Chloe and I decided to have a low-key Friday night and just have some drinks and gossip at the bar of our favorite restaurant.

We went to Ysabel. Normally that place would be filled with young hot guys looking for someone to spend the night with, but that particular night they were completely missing in action. We got there at 10:00 p.m., and after a bowl of French fries and a couple of glasses of champagne, we were ready to go home at 11:30 p.m. "You want to just get to my place and have drinks there?" I asked Chloe, both of us dying of boredom at the bar. "Yes! That is actually a great idea!" We got the check, paid, and were already halfway to the exit when I suddenly decided to use the restroom. "Let's go really quick," I said to her and led the way. Now, if you have ever been to Ysabel, you might remember there is a chair right next to the restrooms, and it is usually always empty, but that time someone was sitting there. I didn't pay attention to who it was, and then I heard a strangely familiar voice calling out my name. I turned around and looked. It took me a second before I realized who was in front of me. "Adam?" I exclaimed, surprised. "Hi." He smiled and seemed very happy to see me. "Hi, Chloe," he said, waving at her. "What are you doing here?" I asked. "Oh, waiting." He shook his head. "My friend is in the restroom," Adam explained. "You might remember him. Tom?" A corner of my lip lifted in a smile, and I glanced at Chloe. Of course we remembered him. Chloe dated the poor guy for two months and treated him like shit. "Anyway, we are going to the bar. You should come join us for old times' sake." "We will," I said, unable to stop smiling.

"What was that?" Chloe asked me as soon as the restroom door closed after us. "What happened to going back to your place?" she asked disapprovingly. "I didn't recognize him. He looks . . ." I was searching for the right word, "different, and weirdly, I don't find him attractive."

"Then why go to the bar with them?"

"Come on, it will be fun," I assured her. She raised her eyebrow, but I knew she was excited to spend an evening with them.

"There they are," Chloe said, pointing to the bar. I didn't know why, but I was nervous. Did I want him to see me and regret he ghosted me all those months ago? Or maybe some little part of me still liked him? "Hey," I said, touching his shoulder. "Oh, there you guys are," he said, standing up from the barstool. "Hi, Tom," I said to his friend. He smiled at me and quickly turned his attention to Chloe. "Here, sit." Adam pointed at the stool he was previously occupying. "So, how have you been?" I asked him. "Things have been good. How's everything with you?" He seemed nervous, and I felt I had an advantage over him. "Things have been great, actually," I said, waving at the bartender. "Yeah? Still seeing that guy?" "What guy?" I asked, flushing and giggling. "Hey, Tom," Adam called out to his friend, "when was it that we saw Sophie?" "You mean when she was making out with that guy? December . . . I think. Yes, December. You went all crazy about it right before Christmas." Tom had obviously said too much, and it was Adam's turn to flush. "So you saw me making out and went crazy, huh?" I asked, unable to hide my amusement. "I didn't go crazy, crazy. Just wasn't prepared for that scene," he said, and I couldn't stop smiling. "That was my boyfriend, and, answering your question, yes, I'm still seeing him." Saying that, I remembered Richard and unwillingly started to compare him to the man sitting in front of me, who used to have such an effect on me and who evidently was one of a few I had feelings for. But now, taking a good look at Adam, it was hard for me to see what I used to see before. I didn't find him charming anymore, or funny, or even attractive, and I thought to myself, Thank God it's Richard and not him. Adam didn't have even half of all the qualities I liked in Richard, and at that moment, I realized that I wouldn't want Richard to change. Even the fighting seemed appealing to me. "What about you? You seeing anyone?" I asked. "I have a girlfriend, actually. We kind of living together," he said without any enthusiasm. "That's great!" I said, giving him the fake smile I specifically developed for this kind of conversation. "Can I have a glass of champagne?" I asked the bartender when he finally paid attention to me. "Make it two, for the pretty lady right there," Adam said, pointing at Chloe, who was enjoying her conversation with Tom way too much. "And place it on my tab," Adam told the bartender. "We are going to Abbey after. You girls should come too. There will be a lot of people you know," he said to me, sipping his beer. A lot of people I knew also meant a lot of people Richard knew, and the last thing I needed was someone telling him they saw Chloe and me with two guys. "I don't know if that's a good idea," I said indecisively. "And by the way, what about your girlfriend? Is she OK with you going out?" I asked, teasing him. "She is in Vegas for a bachelorette party. It's the first time I've been out in months." "That's true," I heard his friend insert, "that girl keeps him hostage in his own apartment," he continued, and Adam flushed again. "Well, you know Tom, that's what a relationship looks like, but actually, sorry, you wouldn't know," I said snarkily. "Ohhh, someone is witty," Tom said, giggling. "Seriously though, you guys should come with us," he continued, "it would be great. We have a lot of catching up to do." Saying that, he glanced at Chloe.

I wasn't sure if we should go with them to the club. Running into a guy you were in love with and just having a little talk in a restaurant was one thing, but going to a club together could have consequences I had no desire to deal with.

"Sophie, let's go! Please," Chloe practically begged me when the guys were paying the bill and almost ready to leave, "it's been so long since we partied. Please!" I didn't know what to do. "What the hell, let's go!" I said after an inner fight with myself. "But we won't stay long, OK?" I made her swear to me on that. We agreed to meet them at the club, making an excuse to take our own Uber and have a chance to discuss everything.

"What am I doing?" I asked myself out loud when the car was pulling over right next to the Abbey. "I need to call Richard," I said to Chloe, taking my phone out of my purse. I dialed his number, but the call went straight to voice mail. I dialed again, the same thing. "Thank you," I heard Chloe say through my thoughts. We were outside the club. "Come on, get out," she told me. The line to get inside was almost a mile long, and then I heard someone yelling out my name. I turned, trying to find who it was. Adam and a bunch of guys were at the door waving at us. "They are with us," Tom said to the bouncer, pointing at Chloe and me. I couldn't stop myself from thinking about Richard. Why didn't he answer my calls? Maybe he was out with some girl? Or maybe even a bunch of girls? My imagination went wild. Fuck it! I said to myself. If he doesn't want to answer, I'm not going to sit and obsess over it. I went out to have fun, and I'm going to do exactly that!

"Sophie?" Adam said. "Sorry, what?" I was lost in my thoughts. "We are doing shots. You in?" Chloe explained. "Hmm . . ." I murmured indecisively, "shots?" I was a lightweight drinker. Shots would make me go full-on crazy, and I was fully aware of that. "Yeah! Let's do shots! I'm in."

I was right, half an hour later and three shots

in, I was completely wasted and dancing with Adam's friend. "What was your name again?" I asked him. "Nick," he said with a smirk on his face. "You can never remember it, can you?" He shook his head. "It's a hard name," I said, trying to find an excuse, but he was right, I was horrible with names. In fact, the only time I would remember someone's name was when I could get something out of it for myself, otherwise, I was not interested even to bother. "We met at least five times already," Nick said, "and every time we both are drunk." He giggled nervously. "Sophie, you wanna do a dinner or something?" "You mean a date?" I stopped dancing. "I dated your friend," I said in disgust. "It's fine, he's fine with it," he said, and I was a bit hurt. "Well, it doesn't really matter, 'cause I have a boyfriend with whom I'm very happy," I said but didn't sound very convincing, even to myself. "OK, cool," he replied simply. "Where is everybody?" I finally noticed that the rest of the group, including Chloe, was gone, and it was only Nick and me. "Let's go find them!" I said in a very bossy manner, almost ordering.

Fifteen minutes later, we finally bumped into them. In the process of that search party, I danced at the strip pole, then was kicked off by some gay performer, did another shot, and flirted with some middle-aged Persian guy who insisted on getting my number. "There you guys are!" I yelled joyfully. Chloe was flirting with Tom, then there was a group of three guys chatting. I knew all of them, but the only one whose name I remembered was Bobby. He had just started his first year as a medical resident at UCLA, and every time we'd met, he would hit on me very hard, and I didn't mind. After all, it's always good to have a doctor as a friend. And then there was Adam and two girls, flirting and laughing. "Oh, these are my friends," he said to them, seeing Nick and me approaching. "Hi, I'm Sophie," I said, waving, "and it's good to know I'm your 'friend,'" I said, turning to Adam. He didn't answer, only smiled nervously.

"Hey, Sophie," Bobby said to me. "Bobby." I smiled. "How's life?" He sounded drunk, perhaps even drunker than I was. "Life's great, thanks for asking," I said, taking a glass from his hand and sipping from it. "We are going to my place for an after-party. You coming?" he asked, biting his lip. "Depends. Who is 'we'?" I asked boldly. "Hmm," he smiled, "you and me, and maybe these two losers," he said and pointed at two of his friends. "Sorry, if Chloe is not going, neither am I." "You can bring her, no biggie," he said quickly. "I'll think about it, Bobby," I said, taking another sip from his glass.

An hour later, the club was closing, and all of us were waiting outside for our Ubers. "Where are we going?" Chloe asked, taking a pause from kissing Tom. "Bobby's," I said, "we are going to Bobby's."

Our group was divided into two different Ubers. In one, Bobby, Nick, and two other guys, and in the second car, Adam in the front seat, and me, Chloe, and Tom in the back. I was wasted, unable to gather together my thoughts, when I suddenly felt an urgent need to call Richard again. I called the number and still no answer. It was 1:45 a.m. on the clock. Any business dinner would be over by then, so it just led me to the conclusion that he had lied to me . . . again. Ten minutes in the car, and I finally realized we were going in a different direction. "This is not the way to Bobby's place," I said, looking out the window. "You would want to go to his place instead, huh?" Adam asked me, irritated. "What is that supposed to mean?" I fired back at him. "He told me," he said, looking at the driver first and then turning back to me. Chloe and Tom were too busy kissing the shit out of each other to listen to our conversation, so that left an intoxicated me, pissed off Adam, and the clueless Uber driver. "Where are we going?" I asked again. "Bobby told me you two fucked," Adam said once again, ignoring my question. "Excuse me, sir," I said, addressing the driver, "I would like to know where we are going, or otherwise I will jump out of this moving car!" I threatened him without any bluff. "Hollywood," Adam answered instead. "We are going to Tom's," he said, taking a deep breath. "Did you?" he asked after a short pause. "Did you two have anything?" "No," I answered shortly, staring out the window and trying to figure out where exactly we were.

My biggest flaw was my impulsiveness, but at the same time, I had a virtue—I could never stay pissed for long. When we got to Tom's place, I had already forgotten the argument I'd had in the car. The only thing I wanted to do that night was to get drunk.

"Do you guys have any stuff on you?" I asked, finishing my second glass of vodka cranberry. "You wanna bump?" Tom asked me, taking a little plastic bag out of his pocket. Of course, they had it on them. In my years in LA, I hadn't met anyone who didn't. . . We bumped, we drank more, we did another line—this time from each other's bodies—and that was when the fun began. High as fuck we started to play truth or dare, but without the truth option. Fifteen minutes into a game, I had no clothes left on. Another ten minutes and we all were sitting there au naturel.

"Shit!" Adam exclaimed, looking at his phone. Apparently, he got three missed calls from his girl. He went to another room to call her back. Of course, the whole conversation is unknown to me, but from what I heard, she was asking him if he was with girls, and he was desperately trying to convince her he was in his bedroom halfway asleep. Hearing that, I chuckled. Adam was in an even more toxic type of relationship than I was. How ironic. He talked to her for thirty straight minutes, and they just ended up yelling at each other and then hung up. "I don't know what to do," he said to Tom, coming back into the living room. His voice was shaking. His eyes were full of tears. I don't know if it was the effect of all the drugs he had done or he was really upset. "I'm afraid she will do something to herself," he said, sitting down and covering his face with both his hands. "She said I would regret it. She said she would kill herself." Shit! The bitch was crazy, I thought to myself. Even I didn't manipulate people that way.

We got back to the game, but the mood was already ruined and was about to be crushed completely. After Adam's crazy girlfriend, it was Richard's turn. When the clock struck 3:40 a.m., he started calling me. "Shhh! Be quiet," I said, "I'm gonna answer." "Don't!" Chloe said to me. "If you pick up, he's gonna ask where you are at. It's almost four in the morning. You are asleep at home. Don't answer!" She was right. Plus, why wasn't he asleep at four in the morning? Would he tell me the same kind of fiction Adam just tried to sell his girlfriend? Richard called four times before he stopped. "Don't answer if he calls again. Don't make the same mistake I did," Adam said to me, lighting a cigarette. I looked at him, realizing that the only mistake I'd made that night was not leaving right after I saw him at Ysabel. I got up from the cushion I was sitting on in the middle of a living room and started getting dressed. "What's wrong?" Tom asked, but "wrong" was absolutely everything. "The fact that I'm here naked, that's what's wrong." "Come on! Don't ruin the night!" Adam said, pissed, sitting absolutely naked, smoking his cigarette. "Chloe, get dressed!" I ordered her. "I'm getting us an Uber, and we are leaving." Suddenly I sobered up and wasn't gonna stay there any longer. And if I was leaving, she was leaving with me. "Get dressed! Now!" I said to her one more time, grabbing her dress from the floor. "Don't be a bitch!" Adam said, looking at me with loathing. "You don't have any morals. But I do! And I'm sorry your relationship sucks, but mine doesn't. And I'm not gonna stay here to continue ruining what I have with the person I love." After that, I just grabbed both Chloe's purse and her hand, and we walked out the door. That night was a closure that came so late. Adam, whom I thought I had feelings for, didn't exist.

I couldn't sleep; cocaine was driving me crazy. Feeling frustration, anger, and anxiety were the side effects of drug abuse at their best. Around 8:00 a.m. I finally fell asleep and was only awakened at 4:00 p.m. by a phone call. "What?" I said in irritation. "You OK?" Richard asked me. Apparently my hungover voice didn't sound charming. "I'm fine, just tired," I said, placing the call on speaker and starting to check my phone. I'd gotten dozens of texts and invitations to the party that night, the same exact party Richard asked me not to go to.

"I called you yesterday," I said, starting my interrogation. "I saw," he said simply, but that answer wasn't going to be sufficient. "Yeah, but why didn't you answer?" I said.

"I told you," he said, sounding irritated, "I had a business dinner! And by the way, I called you back."

"Oh yeah, that reminds me, why were you up at four in the morning, huh? What kind of a business dinner is that? Don't bullshit me." "Take a chill pill," he said, "and call me when you cool off." With that, he just hung up on me, just like that—no answer, no explanation, and if he wanted to play it like that, then I would honor the rules. I got up from bed, took a shower, ordered some junk food, which is literally the only medicine for a bad hangover, and then called Chloe to inform her that later that night she was about to attend a party with me.

Everyone I knew and everyone I wished I'd never met was there. Chloe and I were trying to make our way through the crowd when my phone started ringing. "Hello?" "Where are you?" I heard Richard say. I started to move back, away from the crowd. "I'm out," I said nervously. "You are at the party, aren't you?" He was mad, and I knew that when he gets mad, shit goes down for everyone, "Yes," I said quietly. "After I specifically asked you no to go, huh?" That phrase was a big mistake. It pissed me off. I asked him where he was the previous night and why he was awake at 4:00 a.m. I asked why he didn't answer my calls, and did I get an answer? No, I was told to go take a chill pill. "Look, you don't tell me what to do or where to go and who to go with! And you better remember it!" came out of my mouth before I could even think about it. "Well, good luck tonight. I hope you'll find what you went there for! Don't call me," he said calmly. Without answering, I hung up.

The party was crazy, just like Richard predicted. Suddenly in the middle of all that, the room started to spin. I felt I was going to collapse. Was it the cocaine I did the night before or all the alcohol? I don't know, but I felt like I was going to die in that shitty nightclub. Turning around looking for Chloe, I realized that she was lost somewhere in the crowd. I started moving toward the exit, hoping that the fresh air would do some good. Unfortunately, it had no effect whatsoever. I was walking but had no idea where I was going. Disorientated, I started calling Chloe, knowing perfectly well that the chance she would hear her phone was close to zero. After three attempts, I sat on the ground, pathetically trying to get an Uber and failing every time. It seemed the stars had decided to teach me another lesson. After ten minutes of sitting on the ground with my shoes off, it started to seem that the only option I still had was to call the one who earlier told me not to call him. I dialed Richard's number. "Yes?" To my surprise, I heard his voice right after it started ringing. "Can you come and get me, please?" I cried into my phone. "Please!" "I'll get you an Uber," he said without even asking what was going on or wondering if I was OK. "I'll text you when it's there," he told me with no compassion in his voice. "OK" was all I could say. He hung up and, a minute later, texted me the pic of the car. In fifteen minutes, I was home. I washed off my makeup, turned my phone off, and fell asleep for twelve hours, during which Richard never called or texted or made any effort to check on me. The guy couldn't care less.

Maybe meeting Adam that Friday night was a blessing in disguise after all. The masks were finally off, and whatever was underneath was not pretty.

XX

NOTHING TO BE PROUD OF

If the mirror had the power to show us our character instead of our face, many would have been terrorized by their reflection. Just as at that moment, the reflection of Richard was terrorizing me. Suddenly I realized I didn't know the man I had been with for the past two years. I knew his name was Richard. I knew he worked as an investment banker. I knew he had a brother, and I knew he grew up on the East Side. I knew he had expensive and extravagant taste, and I knew he loved to show off, but I had no clue who that man was. I had often noticed some darkness in him—violence, rage towards others—and yet I simply kept my eyes shut. Now his indifference and cruelty were directed at me, and this time my eyes were wide open.

After the club incident, I fell ill for over a week. My voice was completely gone. I had a high temperature and no idea why it was happening to me or the reason for the illness. I couldn't exactly go visit a doctor since drugs were included, so I decided my only choice was to wait and see what was gonna happen next. Luckily, nothing happened. I got better and in one week's time was out and about again. But the week I had spent at home made me start thinking. Richard had already hurt me for a lifetime or even more, and yet no matter what, I still ran back to him like a loyal puppy whenever he called me. But not this time. No! This time, everything would be different. Because this time, I would repay him for all my tears, hysterics, breakdowns, and anxiety attacks. I would give him a lesson in the elegance of revenge, I just didn't know how exactly.

The first step in my plan was to get my stuff back. Clothes, cosmetics, beauty creams, all of it was still at his house, and if I wanted to be done with him for good, I needed to get all of it out of there. I shot him a text asking very nicely, and he replied in the same manner, agreeing. But instead of sending my things with an Uber, he insisted on dropping them off himself. On D-Day, after staying at home and waiting for him for three hours, I shot another text asking, still very nicely, if he thought he was going to make it that day or if I should have just sent an Uber. He replied as politely as possible, apologizing that he couldn't make it that day and saying he would try sometime next week. A week passed by, and then another one. I texted him again. 'I'm not your driver! I'm busy working and have no time to drive around doing your errands. You need your clothes, come over and pick them up yourself,' he texted me without even a hint of the pretense of niceness from before. I couldn't believe the nerve of the guy. I never asked him to drop them off himself. It was his idea and his initiative. But as it turned out, I knew something about him after all. I knew all his tricks; he was trying to get me into his place. Richard Corbin 101: manipulation was his everything. Too bad for him, I didn't react that time. I ignored his text, deciding that stuff was not that important after all.

One week passed, and another one after that, and now it was Richard's birthday. To understand my anger and frustration, you need to understand that I have always taken birthdays or any celebration in general very seriously. I love to plan parties for people I love and care about. I love to get them the best, most meaningful gifts, and of course, I love to spoil them on their birthday. But even the people I don't know all too well, I always congratulate on social media by writing some nice, touching notes. That year not only didn't I get a gift for Richard, but I also didn't even text him a crappy birthday text, not even 'HB.'

One of the perks of dating, and probably also one of the flaws of it, is that after some time, there are no "my friends" and "your friends," there is only "our friends." You two know the same people, you hang with the same people, you follow the same people on social media, and thanks to IG and everyone's obsession with posting their every single move, you see what those same people are up to. And that day, all of them were invited to a huge party Kai was throwing for his brother's birthday.

Being the only one not invited, I thought I would throw my own little party. I made one of my friends who had a house in The Valley allow me to use their house for my alternate party. I brought Chloe, some other girlfriends, a couple of guys, and most importantly, a DJ. The one thing I am great at is throwing a great party. And everything was going great until after one too many glasses, it was customary, for me to move into my "obsessing over Richard" phase, and in the best of that tradition, I reached that phase once again. "Do you believe it?" I said, asking rhetorical questions and turning the party into a therapy session with a bunch of girls sitting around me, listening to me complaining and go on and on about Richard. I have to admit, my friends were better, more supportive people than I have ever been. If any of them ever obsessed over a guy as much as I did, I would probably stop being friends with them.

I was boring my girls to death for approximate an hour, then the chevalier arrived, saving them by a phone call. I looked at the screen, thinking that my own eyes were deceiving me. Four in the morning and an incoming call from Kai Corbin. I flushed, and my heart rated started to increase. Grabbing my phone, I rushed into another room, trying to avoid curious ears. "Hello?" I asked, answering his call. "Fifi," he said, giggling. His voice sounded sexy, as always. "What are you up to?" Kai asked me, flirting.

"Partying, why?"

"You wanna come and party here?"

"'Here' is where?" I asked, being well aware of his whereabouts.

"I'm at home. We have a bunch of people sleeping around the house, and I remembered you, my Fifi." There it was, a perfect opportunity for my elegant revenge. "If I come, you swear that there is no chance I'll see your brother?" I asked, sobering up in a second and putting my dark mind to work. "Of course not! You think I'm suicidal or what?" "OK then, get me an Uber," I told him in anticipation of what was about to come.

He got a car, and without saying goodbye to any of my friends, I was on my way to implement the plan. I was nervous, anxious, excited, and scared all at the same time. I realized that if Richard saw me there, it would be the end of me, but my desires were far more powerful than fear. Even though I didn't want to admit it to myself, the factor of this crazy rodeo mostly was my love of sex with Kai rather than revenge against Richard, but why not combine business with pleasure?

The car was approaching the house, which I had thought I would probably never visit again. I noticed a dark figure by the garage door, and my heart stopped—it was Richard. I couldn't be mistaken. It looked just like him. I prepared myself mentally and then got out of the car. "Kai!" I said, relieved, coming closer. "Damn, you scared the shit out of me," I spilled, giving him a hug. "Let's go inside," he said, almost whispering. The lights were off, but I could hear people snoring in the living room. I took off my heels, trying to be as quiet as possible. . . Finally, we made it to the bedroom, the same one we'd shared months earlier, and being there felt good, but I knew it was wrong, and it made me wonder, how can something so wrong feel so natural? "I had to see you," Kai said, pulling me closer and kissing me. I could smell the mix of alcohol, Tom Ford cologne, and cigarettes. I loved that smell. "You missed me?" I asked, hanging my arms around his neck. "Yes, have you missed me?" he asked, kissing my cheek and then moving down to my lips and from there to my neck, and down and down.

How is it possible that sex without love always feels better? Love complicated everything, not only in life but also in bed. Kai and I have never loved each other, but he was the best sex partner one could ever ask for, and I'm not even talking about his technique, which, if I'm being completely honest here, had achieved the level of fine art. But most important was the way he made me feel—like the most desired, the most beautiful woman on earth, the most loved, even—in a way other men seemed completely unable to. "God," he said, catching his breath, "I wanted to see you so bad, and now I start thinking about . . ." He took a deep breath. It seemed Kai was sobering up and getting anxious. "What if Richard comes back? He'll kill us both." "Where is he anyway?" I asked, trying to make it sound as if I couldn't care less. "He went to Sam's place with some other friends." "Other friends," an interesting name for girls. "Can you do me a favor?" I said, getting up from the bed and looking for my dress. "Sure, ask away." "Can you go to Richard's room and get my stuff?" For a moment there, he froze, unable to respond. "Are you actually trying to get me killed or something?" he joked, but with some seriousness in his voice. "He will notice, you know." "He wouldn't!" I disagreed. "And even if he asks, you deny everything." "Right," he said sarcastically, pulling up his pants, "why don't you just call him and ask for your stuff?" "Like I haven't tried," I said in irritation. "OK, I've got to go before your brother comes back and decapitates both of us." "It's probably a good idea," Kai said. "Maybe I can stop by later at your place, and we have lunch or something," he murmured. "Or something?" I smiled, biting my lip. "Yeah," he smiled too. "OK, let's get you an Uber."

We walked through the back door to the car. The sun was up, and everything looked and felt different. "I hate to let you go now," Kai said, leaning closer to me. "See you later today?" I asked, kissing his cheek. "You bet," he said, then kissed me on the lips.

By the time I got home, I had regretted seeing Kai one hundred times over and had made one hundred excuses for myself.

And since he never called me that day, I figured he regretted that night as well. In two weeks, he left the country to go for a business trip, and his post of an IG story was the only reason I found out about it at all. With Kai gone, I decided to forget that night ever happened and just move on, but in order to do that, first I needed to have some BFF's therapy and discuss every delicious detail of that night.

"That is awesome!" Chloe said with energy when I finished the story. "I don't feel the way I thought I would," I confessed, "I thought it would give me closure." "I don't think there is such thing as 'closure,'" she disagreed. "I don't know, maybe you're right." I stopped for a second, thinking about my actions, and at that moment, my phone blinked. I got the most unexpected message. Richard texted me, saying I had to come and pick up my stuff. "Don't go!" Chloe said to me in a bossy manner, "Sophie, no, you can't fall for it!" "I won't! I have no desire to see him or deal with his bullshit ever again," I said, genuinely believing it myself. One text, and another, and another, and now Richard was threatening to leave my stuff outside the garage unless I came to pick it up. 'Fine, I'll come with my friends, and they will go inside to get it from you,' I texted him. 'No! I don't need your crazy friends here!' He was doing what he did best—manipulating.

"I have to go," I said to Chloe, looking at myself in the mirror and trying to fix my unfixable hair. "No! it's not a good idea," she protested. "It's easier this way. I'll go there, pick it up, and never have to deal with him again," I said confidently. "Yeah, yeah, just don't stop texting me when you get there," she said. "What do you think is going to happen there, huh?" I chuckled. "He'll kidnap me or something?" I said sarcastically and shook my head. "What usually happens when you see him." She sounded very confident about it, perhaps even too confident. "Nothing will happen because I don't want anything with him anymore," I reassured Chloe. She smirked and nodded.

I texted Richard that I was on my way, and he only replied 'OK.' I pulled into the driveway of that so familiar house. Thank God the walls couldn't talk. The door was open. "Hey?" I said, walking in. "Hi, Sophie." I heard Richard's voice, but no sight of him. "I'm in the living room," he said. "Hi," I said when he finally appeared in front of me. The TV was on, and some random guy I'd never seen before was sitting in front of the TV, fully ignoring my presence. "You go ahead upstairs. I'll be there in a minute, OK?" I nodded, not really knowing why I would need him upstairs, since it would only take ten minutes to get all of my stuff and get out of that house forever. I went to the bathroom first. All of my stuff that used to be on shelves now was hidden under the sink. I grabbed all the bottles, all the creams and lotions, and even my toothbrush.

When I was in the closet, I heard Richard coming up the stairs. "How have you been?" he asked me, sitting down on the bed. "Pretty good, you?" "Not too bad," he said quietly. I walked out of the closet with two huge bags. "You have lots of stuff here, huh?" he chuckled. "I guess," I said, looking down at my bags. "Can we talk?" he said. "I need to finish something with that guy downstairs. It's work-related, and it has a deadline, but I really need to talk to you, please?" I didn't know how to answer. I wasn't sure what to say because I wasn't sure if I wanted him to talk. What more could be said here? "What do you want to talk about?" I asked straightforwardly. "About us, what else?" I looked at him without saying anything. Was there any "us" left? I didn't know. After everything we did to destroy it, would it be possible to repair this relationship? "Please," he said again, after getting no reply. "OK, I'll wait," I said, looking at him. "Thank you!" Richard said, and a smile appeared on his face. He then took a step closer to me and tried to kiss my cheek, but I turned my face away from him. "No, don't," I said very quietly. "Sorry," he said, taking a step back, "I will be done in thirty minutes tops, and then we'll talk." Then he left the room.

Taking a deep breath, I sat down on the bed. What was I doing? Why agree to that? Was I still expecting a possibility of us getting back together? Or even worse, did I want to get back together? My brainwork was interrupted by a text—it was Chloe, whom I had totally forgotten to text. 'Everything is fine,' I texted her. 'Are you still there?' I could read disapproval in her text. 'I am, but I'm leaving soon. He wants to talk.' 'Bad idea! Very bad idea,' she texted. As much as I appreciated her support, it was getting annoying. Somehow all of my friends always thought they knew my needs, my feelings, and how I should live my life better than I did. And perhaps it was my mistake. Maybe I was oversharing with them, and with time it had escalated from support to giving unwanted advice with absolutely no boundaries. 'I'll be fine,' I texted her back, turning my phone screen down and lying on the bed.

When you are dealing with Richard, you quickly notice he is not a very punctual person, and whenever he gives you an estimated time, you have to multiple it by two or sometimes even by three. That time was no different; his "thirty minutes tops" turned out to be more than an hour. "I'm sorry, it took me so much longer than I thought," he said, walking into the bedroom, where I had already turned on the TV and was watching some crappy show. "You wanted to talk," I said, turning the TV off, "talk then." I took my sneakers off, placing my feet on the bed. "Well, first of all, thank you for agreeing to talk," he said very politely. That was his special skill, he could be Prince Charming if it benefited him. "You are welcome," I said with an iron voice. "Look, I know I made you unhappy." He sounded nervous. "But maybe we can work it out." "I was sick!" I said to him, irritated. "I was sick, and you didn't even text to check on me. And I know what you are about to say next, you were angry, but that's exactly the point of a relationship, you don't bail on a person because you are mad at them! For some reason, it's fundamentally hard for you to be with someone." I stopped, looking him in the eyes and waiting for an explosion. "I know. You are right," he said instead. I didn't expect the response I got. "I feel that every time I really need you, you are not there, and I keep asking myself if it's even worth doing. If I can't rely on you, what's the point of all this?" I said, feeling that my heart was dropping. "I can do better," he said simply. "I'll try to do better." A promise was made, but I wasn't sure he had any intention of keeping it. "I want to believe you, and trust me, I know there are a lot of things you hate in me. You . . ." I stopped, trying to think of something Richard couldn't stand in me, "you always say I argue with you, and you get mad when I fall asleep during a movie, and you hate a lot of other things in me." "I don't hate anything in you," he said very calmly. "My point is we are not perfect, but before it was different, before you were there for me, but now something has changed. I don't know this part of you." "Are you saying you don't love me anymore?" Richard said, jumping to conclusions. "No, that's not what I'm saying," I said, taking a breath, "I love you, but I don't like you." I could feel the tension in the air, and then the silence was broken. "I still love you, too, and I want to try again," he said, ignoring the main context of my previous statement. After it was said, I realized it was the first time he had actually told me he loved me. Somehow before, our feelings went without saying—it was a universal truth—but now the cat was out of the bag.

We talked till six in the morning, going back and forth until we passed out fully dressed. The next morning, we agreed to try again, no matter how hard it might get. We agreed to talk to each other about our feelings like normal couples do instead of acting out. We agreed to try and grow together. He was optimistic about it. I was trying to be optimistic as well, but the little voice in my head was doubting we would be able to change anything, and, well, it turned out the voice was right after all.

XXI

DELUSIONLAND

"You are back together?" Chloe asked me in frustration when I called her the next morning after meeting Richard. "Yes, we are. And you don't have to be so judgmental about it," I noted. "How many times are you going to continue this?" I didn't appreciate the attitude I was getting. "I'm just telling you a fact, not asking for permission," I said to her. "Seriously? The way he treats you and the way he treats your friends, and you still can't see that the guy is toxic?" she almost yelled. "I'm not going to discuss it! You have some issues with yourself and your dating life, and now you are trying to turn it from yourself to me! You can't stand the fact I have a man in my life who actually cares about me, who doesn't look just for sex like always happens in your case!" I knew it was a hurtful thing to say to a friend, but at that moment, I wanted to hurt her. "Are you kidding right now? Do whatever the fuck you want, just don't call me the next time he mistreats you! I'm tired of listening to the same drama for two years now!" Chloe yelled at me. "Oh yeah, like your life is fucking wonderland! I'm sick of all the bullshit I have to keep taking from you." On that note, we ended the conversation, and at that moment, it seemed our friendship with it.

Week after week, argument after argument, Chloe was right, I was miserable with Richard. We fought every day, broke up, made up, and then pressed repeat. Every time we had a disagreement, he would say it was because I "loved to argue." I was unhappy like never before; Richard was suffocating me, and the worst part, I had put myself in the position. Everything I did seemed to piss Richard off, and everything he said would irritate me. We were living in an actual nightmare, both of us, and we were the creators of it. It was exhausting, it was unhealthy, and I couldn't keep up with it any longer. I promised myself not to give up on our relationship, but if keeping that promise meant giving up on my mental health, it was a promise not worth keeping. After another fight, when I stormed out of his house and decided to take a walk, I made a tough choice. The fresh air had cleaned my mind, and I knew it was finally the time to move on. 'I have been giving it a lot of thought, and I think it's better for us to stop this charade. I'm not happy, and I haven't been happy for a very long time now. We need a break, and I'm sure you feel the same way.' It took me an hour to write those couple of sentences and twice that long to finally press the send button. And, just like that, I had separated myself from Richard . . . again.

It was the middle of summer, and I was spending it at home, reading, watching Netflix, and avoiding everyone. Even though Chloe was partially right, I wasn't going to be the first one to make a move and apologize. She pissed me off good that time. But without Richard and without Chloe, I realized I didn't have that many people whose company I really enjoyed. Mia was working a lot, some girls I used to know from my previous job were only fit to party with, I was still without an occupation, living off my family's money, and I had no desire to change anything. I was a lost sheep. Not knowing what I wanted, and until I found it again, I decided to stay home together with my thoughts and my TV.

Surprisingly, those turned out to be the best moments I had experienced in a very long. We manage to forget how precious the time we spend with ourselves is. When we don't have families, kids, we take it for granted or even sometimes hate it, when in fact we should appreciate it to the fullest, since it only lasts so long. That summer, I was doing exactly that. No friends, no boyfriends, no bullshit. I loved it. Another couple of weeks and it was Chloe's birthday. We still were on non-talking terms, but she was my best friend, and I decided to be a grown-up and text her. I wished her a happy birthday, and, in a minute, she invited me to the birthday celebration dinner. I didn't buy her a present, and it was too late to go shopping, so I just got a huge bouquet and an envelope full of cash. After all, some say cash is the best present.

"Hey," I said, smiling when we first saw each other at the restaurant. "Hi," Chloe said softly and went for a hug. I felt at home. As good as those weeks of solitude were, I had missed her. I'd missed my best friend, our gossip, our stupid jokes no one else would understand. I missed having someone I could tell everything. "You were right," I said when we finished dinner and moved to the bar, "I mean about Richard. You were right." Chloe raised her eyebrow. I knew what was going on in her mind, but she chose not to say it out loud. "And this time, it's for good," I promised, but she was still not saying anything, and I couldn't figure out why. Chloe waved to the bartender, ordering another tequila pineapple, and after finishing it in one go, she finally started talking. "I need to tell you something," she said, frightening me to the core. "What? Something bad?" I asked, worrying. "Something about Richard." She stopped for a moment, taking a breath and gathering her courage.

"He went out with Ursula." When I heard that sentence, time stopped. He went out with Ursula, he went out with Ursula, he went out with Ursula . . . The words echoed in my head. The world around me stopped existing. Ursula . . . Then I got a flashback to one of those Hollywood movies. On the same day a year ago, Chloe had taken us all to Vegas, and Ursula was there. I had never hated a single soul until the day I met Ursula. She was the most annoying, exhausting, irritating, unbearable person in the whole world, and Chloe's friend. We were in the hotel room getting ready for a night out when Ursula asked me,

"Do you know anyone named Richard?" It caught me off guard—of course, I knew him, the question was, how did she know him? Apparently, when Richard was in Europe, he decided to add every single girl I knew to his Instagram collection, and that bitch Ursula happened to be one of them. I remembered telling her he was my ex-boyfriend, and I remembered her saying she wouldn't accept his follow request. I also remembered the conversation I had with Richard when we got back together. I told him about the trip and about Ursula and how horrible she made me feel every time I saw her. And I remembered him saying it was she who had sent him a follow request, not the other way around, and I remembered him saying he was never interested in her. "Sophie . . . Sophie?" Chloe's voice dragged me back to reality. "He fucked her?" I asked her straight. She nodded. "I was at her place, her phone was on a table, and I noticed him sending her a DM on Instagram," Chloe said quietly with guilt in her voice. "What did he say?" "He asked if she was coming over. After that, I asked her how she knew him. She said he texted her on Instagram, they went on a date, and he took her to his place. She said they only had sex twice." "When was it?" "Three weeks ago." She looked at me, and I noticed tears in her eyes. "I wanted to call you but didn't know how to say it." Chloe burst into tears, and I felt nothing, as if my heart wasn't in my chest anymore. Instead, it was in some box buried six feet underground, preventing me from feeling a thing. "Knowing what a whore your friend is, let's just hope she didn't reward him with some STDs," I said without any emotion. "I'm so sorry," Chloe whispered. "No, don't be! It's OK," I said, not knowing who I was trying to convince more, her or myself. With that, we stopped talking about it and started drinking heavily, finishing the party at 6:30 a.m. at Chloe's place.

In the morning, she had an early flight to Miami. She left for the airport at 7:30, dropping me off on the way. I took a shower, had breakfast, closed the drapes, crumpled into my bed, and started crying. My heart was back in my chest, and I felt miserable. I cried for six days, not leaving my bedroom, eating junk, and not talking to anyone again. The thing that hurt me was not the cheating. In fact, it wasn't really cheating, since it happened when we were broken up. I was hurt because it was Ursula he chose. The girl seemed to like my leftovers, since Richard was the third guy she went out with after I was done with them. I couldn't care less about the other two, but with Richard, everything was different. He was off-limits to everyone but me.

After a week of depression, when my dark circles got bigger than my circle of friends, I knew it was time to get back out there.

Some say love is blind. In fact, it's deaf, dumb, and blind. . . I started to remember things, things that didn't bother me at the time but which now fell into place like puzzle pieces. Like that time when I found a ring in Richard's bedroom, and he pretended to have no idea whose it was, saying that probably one of Kai's friends left it there; or that story with that T-shirt in the drawer; or that one time when he lied to me, pretending to go to his friend's birthday and going out to a club instead; or the story with the ice cream and a check that showed "table for 2." And those were only the tip of the iceberg, some little things that I did know. I was terrified to think how much more was hidden from me.

From the moment I learned I was living in delusion and denial, I was determined to change my life, to change the people in it, starting with blocking Richard everywhere he appeared. I know it was immature and dramatic, but I was so hurt that any communication with him seemed unbearable at the time. It came down to the ridiculous point where I even blocked his email. And then one day, when I thought I was safe from him, I received an unexpected surprise in the mail—a package that was addressed to Richard. After being confused at first, I realized that some time ago he asked to use my address for some of his correspondence and that without any second thoughts, I had agreed. Now I would have to deal with it. I was punished for my kindness yet again. Even the thought of talking to or seeing Richard was painful. No, I wouldn't torture myself, not for him or his stupid package. Instead, I planned everything thoroughly. I would give the package to Chloe for her to give to Ursula and then text Richard about it. The next day, thirty minutes before meeting with Chloe to execute my plan, I texted him, making sure he was still blocked and wouldn't be able to reply. I took a picture of the envelope and wrote below, 'I'm gonna leave it with Chloe, and she'll pass it to Ursula, let her know when you're coming to pick it up. Sure, you know the address.' I felt good, even empowered, pressing send, but my triumph didn't last. In less than ten minutes, my Vibe app started ringing. It was Richard. The blood rushed through my veins, but my heart had stopped beating. I rejected the call, but he wouldn't stop at that, texting instead, 'Hi, please don't give it to anyone. I'll come to pick it up.' Reading this, I started panicking, and that panic grew into an anxiety attack. Seeing him would kill me. I wasn't strong enough for that. In response to his text, I blocked his number on Viber too, but I also decided not to give the package to Ursula. After all, I didn't know what was inside.

That story messed me up pretty good, but with Richard now blocked, this time everywhere, I could finally start breathing again. And not only that, I got Bumble and was swiping left and right. But being mentally unstable before, now I was walking on the edge, and it was a matter of time before I was going to break down again. It was obvious I needed help, but instead, I decided to get a rebound. After only two days on the app, I got a date. Some guy in whom I had absolutely no interest except physically. We met only once, during which time I managed to get completely drunk, talk all night about my ex, and then fuck him like there was no tomorrow. I have to admit, it did make me feel better, even if it was for a short period of time, like a bandage on a bleeding wound.

After weeks of distractions, I decided the only way I would really be able to move on was to face my problem. I opened my email, and there in the spam folder, I had a dozen massages from Richard asking me to open his mail and send him pics of it. If that was what it would take for us to be done, then I didn't have any choice but to do it. I went to my bedroom, opened the envelope, and inside there were at least seventy pages of some paperwork. God damn it, I would have to spend at least an hour taking pics and sending them to him. When I was halfway through, Richard, as if he had some magical sixth sense, emailed, 'Hi, I need to talk to you about something. Please unblock me.' Reading it my heart started racing again, the anxiety returned, I couldn't breathe, the room was spinning—the thought of talking to him crashed me. Unable to stand, I dropped to the floor, starting to cry hysterically. 'I don't want to talk to you, let alone see you! Just email me what you need, and I'll do it, but please leave me alone after that' was my response to him. The only thing it seemed he wanted were the pics, so I finished what I started. 'I shared it in iCloud with you, check your texts, and please don't bother me anymore.' It was done, I was free now.

But perhaps there was still a valuable lesson left for me to learn because life seemed to be unwilling to let Richard and I walk in different directions. When it finally felt like the end of our story, another package came in the mail. This time I emailed Richard myself without hesitating. He asked for the pics again and repeating the process, I was confident it was finally the epitaph. But life wasn't giving up; it had a very mean and weird sense of humor. It seemed to like to torture us. Or maybe it was my punishment . . . another package came, and then another, and another. I was bleeding inside out, and someone upstairs seemed to enjoy it. No doubt it was my punishment—karma working at its best. Maybe I did deserve it. Maybe the punishment was fit for the crime . . .

XXII

CAN WE EVER BE DONE?

End of August. Richard unblocked, all the paperwork he ever received had been photographed and sent to him, and now whenever Richard felt like talking to me, he would use the line 'Hi, received anything for me?' as an opener. 'Hi,' I texted him back one day, 'if I had, I would have sent it to you by now.' 'Thanks. I know, you are the best!' was the response I got. The whole thing was turning into flirting from both sides. The worst part was that I saw him and Ursula every time I closed my eyes.

I couldn't stop thinking and obsessing over it, and how was one supposed to move on like that? I was stalking him on social media. I didn't want him back, but the thought of him moving on and being with someone else was hurtful to me. Perhaps it was the same for him. A psychologist would get so rich on us—two cases impossible to solve. Maybe that's why we could never let go of each other, and maybe it was time to face the truth: in our relationship, we were two toxic people, not one, as I used to think before. And maybe we were together for a reason. Maybe we needed to learn a lesson. It was a quest, we were tested, and whoever passed the test would be able to move on, and until then, we would be tormented and taught.

"We should go on vacation," Chloe said, passing me a glass of sangria and sitting next to me on the couch. "Hawaii? Or maybe the Caribbean." She was thinking out loud. "Yeah, who's gonna pay for the vacation?" I asked, chuckling. "We'll find some hot guys who'll pay and go with us." "Right," I giggled, "I like the plan." "Here's to the plan." She raised her glass. We both needed a break. That Friday night, we stayed inside drinking the homemade sangria I had prepared earlier and watching *Sex and the City*. It was a good evening until I ruined it. My addiction to social media and my constant need to stalk Richard took over me. "Oh God!" I screamed, staring at my phone. "What?" Chloe asked without any enthusiasm. "We need to go out!" I said, exhilarated. "What?" Chloe repeated, this time with more emotion. "Why?" "Richard is at Skybar with a bunch of people we know," I explained my motives. "No! Sophie, come on," but I was already past the point of no return. "Please! Come with me," I begged, "just for two hours, please." But Chloe was unyielding, and she had no intention of giving in. "I'm too tired to go anywhere, and even if I weren't, I wouldn't! You don't need this," she tried to reassure me. Realizing that tactic wasn't working, I tried another. "I need closure. I can't move on until I get one.

You can help me to move on!" I paused, analyzing Chloe's reaction. "If you don't come with me, I'll go alone and will look stupid, and God knows what I might do." I looked her straight in the eye. For a moment there, the room got very quiet. "Damn you! Go get ready and pick me up on the way," she finally gave in. "I love, love, love you!" I screamed, almost jumping on her with a hug. "Yeah, you owe me one!"

I got an Uber and rushed home. The task before me was not an easy one. I needed a dress that screamed, "I'm the best thing that ever happened to you, and it's your loss we aren't together, and you will end up alone, and I will end up with a hot young billionaire"—too big of a task, too little of time. Never have I ever in my life gotten ready so fast. I ended up choosing a little black dress. After all, classic is always good, plus my period was due any day now, and it made my boobs look at least two sizes bigger than usual. 'I'm on my way,' I texted Chloe, running in heels from the front door to the Uber. Ten thousand thoughts a second were rushing through my head. Maybe it was the biggest mistake of my life. What if it won't give any closure but will have quite the opposite effect on me? Lost in my thoughts, I didn't notice how we made it to Chloe's place. I dialed her but got no reply, then dialed again and again. "Hello?" She sounded disoriented. "You fell asleep, didn't you?" I said. "No, no, where are you?" I knew she fell asleep. "I'm downstairs in the car, waiting for you! Hurry up." Three minutes later, I saw a figure walking out of the front door holding a mug in her hands and shak-

ing from side to side. The time I spent picking an outfit Chloe spent finishing the sangria. "What's that?" I
asked, pointing at the mug when she got into the car.

"Wine," Chloe said, taking a sip. "I got so anxious. You want?" she offered. The truth: I was beyond
anxious, and the wine sounded perfect. "Yes." I took
the mug from her. The wine was so strong I felt tipsy
after the first sip. "What am I doing, Chloe?" "What
do you mean?" She was confused, and so was I. "Going there to see him. Maybe it's wrong, you know.
I'm not sure anymore." I did another sip, this time
a bigger one. "Look, we go there, and if you want to
leave, we leave right away, OK?" She smiled, taking
my hand in hers. In theory, the plan sounded perfect,
but we forgot a teeny-tiny detail. By the time we got
to Skybar, we were already drunk on wine, and when
we are drunk, that usually is the beginning of some
crazy-ass story.

"Come on, let's go!" Chloe was yelling, getting
out of the car. "Wait! How am I supposed to go in
with the mug?" We looked at each other and burst
into laughter. I placed the cup on the street, right next
to the sidewalk, and then, taking a deep breath, we
made our approach. The line to get in was enormous,
so we just skipped it, going straight to the front. "Hi,"
I said to the bouncer flirtatiously. "Good evening, ladies." He looked at me from head to toe and opened
up the rope. "Enjoy," he said, smiling. At that moment, I knew I had made the right choice with the
dress. "We have been here for fifteen minutes, and

they just skipped the line," I heard a group of girls complaining when we were already halfway inside. The club was full. I didn't remember seeing that many people there in a very long time. "Do you see him?" I asked Chloe as we moved toward the first bar. "No, not yet," she said, very concentrated. "Excuse me?" I heard someone approaching me.

"Yes?" I said, turning around. "I just wanted to say, you are very beautiful." This boosted my ego. Among things I loved to do, taking compliments was at the top of my list. "Well, thank you," I said, turning back around with a ghost of a smile on my face. "Would you like a drink?" the guy asked. I needed a drink, and if the first time my ex and I were to see each other, I was also accompanied by a guy, that would be even better. "I would love a drink. And so would my friend," I said, pointing at Chloe.

We had spent approximately fifteen minutes at that bar and still no sign of Richard. "Where is he?" I asked Chloe nervously. "Ohhh," she exhaled, noticing someone in the crowd. "It's him?" I asked. "No, his friend." "Who needs his friend?" I snapped. "Let's go walk around. We need to find him." And just like that, ignoring the nice guy who got us drinks, we started to make our way through the crowd. "He's probably at the other bar," I suggested, "let's go check it out." The place was so crowded that it was challenging to move around, but on the bright side, not a single man could stop looking at me and my hormonal boobs.

When we finally made it to the second bar upstairs, all that was waiting there was a disappointment. "I don't see him anywhere," I said, looking around. But since we had already made our way up there, we might as well get drinks. Right when I was about to lose hope, Chloe whispered to me, "Don't turn; he is on your right at that table by the wall." "Did he notice us?" I asked, looking in the opposite direction. "He's looking at you right now," Chloe said; she was, without doubt, the best spy. "Good! Let's get our drinks and walk away," I told her. The game was on, and I'd made the first move.

We got our drinks and went downstairs back into the crowd, sat on a couch right in the middle of the room, making sure it was the most visible one, and it took less than a minute for two guys to approach asking if it was OK to sit next to us. They weren't good-looking, but they were an important component in that operation. Another five minutes and I saw Richard walking down the stairs and looking around, and after noticing me, coming straight my way. "I'm glad you two made up!" he said, looking at Chloe and me. "I'm sorry?" I said. "You want something?" I sounded cold, arrogant. "No, nothing," he answered. "I see you have company to keep yourselves entertained." He glanced at the two guys who were still sitting on the couch right next to us. "Enjoy your night, Sophie." After saying that, he just walked away. That's it? I thought to myself, and for that, I dressed up and did my makeup in less than thirty minutes? But it wasn't the end; not just yet. The night was still young. I flirted with every guy who dared to talk to me, and Chloe, meanwhile, was spying on Richard, making sure we were in his sight. "I'll go to the bar to get some water; you need anything?" she asked me. "No, thanks. I'm good," I said as she walked away. I saw a guy walking toward me. Bingo! He was exactly what I needed. Tall, fit, very good-looking, and very young" Hi." His voice was soft. "Hey," I said, smiling. "I like your dress," he said. A lame open-er, but who cared, he was too cute to even listen to what he was saying. "Thanks, I like it too," I chuckled. "What's your name?" I asked, sipping my cocktail. "I'm Alex, and you?" "Sophie." After ten minutes of talking to Alex, I started to like him, not only was he good-looking; but he was interesting, which is so rare in men these days. "Oh, finally," I said, noticing Chloe, "this is my friend Chloe." I introduced them, "Hi, I'm Alex." He shook her hand. The rest of the night I spent in Alex's company, totally forgetting why I had come to Skybar in the first place.

"Richard is circling around you like falcon around prey," Chloe told me when Alex went to the bar to get us all drinks. "I'm so happy we came here, Chlo. Maybe I needed to come so I could meet this nice, smart, funny guy." She smiled at me. "Thanks for being here with me," I whispered, smiling back at her. Talking, drinking, laughing, and getting to know Alex, I didn't even notice that three hours had flown by. It was already 2:00 a.m., and everyone was getting kicked out of the club. "Ready to go?" Alex asked, offering a hand and helping me to get up from the couch. "Thank you," I said, taking his hand. Handsome, smart, funny, and gallant—the full package, if you ask me. As we were walking toward the door, out of nowhere, Richard appeared right next to me with three girls by his side. I recognized them immediately. They were the same tacky group we'd seen at the door, the ones who complained about us getting in before them. Well, apparently, that was the best he could do. "Get lucky tonight," he whispered to me when we came alongside. "Don't worry about me." I smiled, moving forward, away from him.

"Where do you want to go now?" Alex asked when we had finally made it outside. "Habibi," I exhaled. He took us to Habibi. We danced and kissed till morning. It seemed I had found a new crush. He was everything I was looking for in a man, plus a bonus—he was a great kisser. In my experience, if a guy knew how to kiss you, he usually also knew how to do the rest of the job.

I got home at six in the morning, and before I got the chance to even take my clothes off and jump into the shower, Alex called me. We talked for a good two hours. It was official: Richard was moving into oblivion, and I could thank Alex for this.

That Saturday night, I spent very quietly, inviting Mia over for homemade dinner. After a crazy Friday, I needed a rest, so we just stayed in my place doing tarot readings, something only people in LA believe in. By 10:00 p.m. we called it a night, and before I even knew it, I was knocked out in my bed. But then, early Sunday morning, after almost twenty-four hours, Alex called again, this time asking me on a date. It wasn't my ideal vision of a perfect first date. He took me to a street-food festival, and you can call me spoiled, but normally my first dates were hosted at Tao, Katana, Maestro's, Nobu, and definitely not at a food truck on 8th and Central. The age difference between this boy and the men I had usually dated was felt right then and there. He was only twenty-three, after all. On our date, I learned that Alex was from Brooklyn but was planning on moving to LA in a couple of months and had come to explore the city and find a place to move into later on. I have to admit, I liked him more when I was drunk. He was still cute and smart and funny, just not as much so as I had first thought... Our date ended with a kiss and a promise of a phone call.

In the next two weeks, promises were broken left and right. Alex never called, and Richard, though he had agreed to leave me alone, seemed to have had a change of heart.

"What?" I asked, irritated, picking up the phone when he called for the fifth time in a row. "Hi, Sophie." He sounded nervous, like a little boy. "How are you?" "I'm good. You need anything?" I asked straightforwardly. "Just thought I would give you a call to see how you're doing." "OK," I said indecisively, not knowing how to respond that my feelings hadn't changed, I was still hurt, and I had absolutely no desire to put myself through hell again. "Richard, I don't know if I gave you some wrong impression that I wanted to be in communication with you, but I'm not looking for that," I said from the heart, and once I had opened my mouth, there was no way I would shut it. "You were cheating on me constantly, and I was too in love and too blind to see things clearly. For fuck's sake . . ." I stopped. "You even even managed to cheat on me with Ursula." "I haven't!" he argued, but it was the wrong move because, in a second, I went from slightly irritated to an atomic bomb that was about to blow up. "Shut up!" I screamed at him. "Just shut up! I'm so tired of all your lies! You don't know what being in a relationship means. You have no idea what being loyal to your partner means! You hurt me so bad. You ruined two years of my life!" I continued screaming, letting out all the anger that had built up inside of me, "You know what," I paused for a second, "don't ever call me again! I don't want to hear from you again." "Are you serious?" It seemed Richard couldn't believe his own ears. "Delete my number and never call me again!" With that, I hung up. At the moment, I didn't even know if I really meant it, and despite my expectations, the scene I had just performed didn't make me feel any better; on the contrary, I sat down on my bed and lost myself to this weird listless feeling.

For the whole week, my biggest achievement of the day was getting up in the morning. I felt apathetic, depressed, and unwilling to do anything except lie in my bed all day watching some unrealistic Netflix show.

"I think it's a very good thing for you!" my friend Iris said over a glass of wine at Wally's when we met to do some catching up. She was the wisest and most mature friend I had, and she was always giving me good advice. In fact, she was the only one whose advice I actually listened to. My principle in life was and until this day remains that good relationship advice can only come from someone who's married, has kids, and is actually happy with their partner. Iris was one of those people. "You don't think it was harsh? I mean, I know that it's the right thing to do, but still," I mumbled. "Listen, the man doesn't know what he wants, and not only does he confuse himself, he also confuses you." I knew she was right. "And what do you think about this guy? Alex?" I jumped from the subject. "I didn't even like him that much. He took me to eat hot dogs on a first date, and now he's the one not calling," I said, disappointed. "The right guy will come along," she said, trying to cheer me up. "You are a smart, beautiful girl. When the time is right, you'll meet a nice guy." "Yeah, right," I said, uncertain. "And what about you? How's work?" Having no desire for psychoanalysis, I changed the subject. We gossiped, then had a deep conversation, then we gossiped again, and without even knowing it, I was already on my third glass. "Can you believe this guy?" I murmured, taking a sip of my Sauvignon Blanc. "Which one?" Iris asked. "Alex!" "Oh no, we're right where we started," she said, tired. "Took me on some cheap-ass date and hasn't even called!" "Well, you said he's moving, right?" I nodded. "Maybe he just got caught up in the process. You know how exhausting it can be." "You're right!" I said and reached for my purse. "What are you trying to do?" Iris asked, concerned. "I'll text him myself." I was confident. "After all, if the mountain will not come to Muhammad, well, you know the rest." I got my phone out and texted him a simple 'Hi, how are you.' "Just to give him a head's up," I said, smiling, very proud of myself and my determination. After that, all I had to do was wait, and so I waited, fifteen minutes, twenty, thirty. "Why didn't you stop me?" I complained. "As if there were a way to," Iris said quietly. "You know what I always liked in Richard?" "What?" she asked, just being polite but with absolutely no real desire to know. "Because, unlike many guys, he would always text back very fast. That was his best quality. I bet if I text him now, he will reply in a minute," I said, and as the words escaped my mouth, the idea was born. "No!" Iris said, as if knowing exactly what it was I was thinking at that moment. "Yes!" I exclaimed and started texting Richard. All those speeches about not wanting him in my life went to waste in a blink of an eye when I texted him. It was one word, 'hi,' and just as I predicted, I got a reply in less than a minute. Looking at my phone, I couldn't stop smiling. "You see, I told you," I said victoriously. "You sure did." She didn't sound as excited about it as I was. Richard was very sweet, but that night things didn't go further than small talk. I saw Iris's disapproval when she dropped me off. Even though she didn't say anything, I could tell with just one look at her that she disapproved. "Take care," she said as we said our goodbyes. "Thank you for the evening and for listening to me,"

I said, feeling a little guilty for talking all night about my problems. "Any time," she said, smiling softly.

In the lobby, while I was waiting for the elevator, I couldn't stop thinking about Richard, and then I heard my phone beep. I reached for it, full of excitement, hoping it was a text from him. "Oh," I exhaled with disappointment, finding it was only Alex texting me back.

"So, you texted him yourself?" Chloe giggled. "It's pure comedy." And she was right, the whole thing seemed like some Brazilian soap opera. Thinking about it, I started giggling myself. "Yes, I texted him after I told him never to call me again." That day I came to Chloe's new workplace to have lunch with her at Century City Mall. We planned to check out some stores, as well as cute lawyers, investment bankers, and talent agents, and I was secretly hoping I might run into Richard, since his office was close by as well. "I think he'll call me today or tomorrow and invite me on a date," I said as we walked down the shopping aisles at Nordstrom. "Do you want him to?" "I don't know what I want, that's the problem," I told her honestly. "He has his flaws, yes, but I look at other guys, and Richard doesn't seem as half as bad." "And what about Ursula?" Chloe asked, and I felt like my wound was starting to bleed again. "Don't say that name!" I said, raising my voice. "Never say that name to me!" Even though I was halfway to forgiving Richard, I had neither the will nor desire to forgive that sneaky bitch. "OK, not saying any names, sorry," Chloe said, trying on Chanel flats. "You like it?" she asked, pointing at her feet. "Yes, that's nice," I answered without even looking. The only thing I had on my mind was Richard.

Maybe my thoughts materialized, or maybe I'd sent them to Richard by the invisible channel between us, but the next morning I woke up to a 'Good morning, how are you?' text from him. I replied, saying that I was good, and asked how things were with him, and after brief small talk, he invited me to have lunch with him. I was beyond happy but didn't want to allow him even the slightest glimpse of my satisfaction, so I texted, 'All of a sudden? Haha, well OK, I don't mind getting lunch with you,' and with this fake indifference, I started to get ready. I tried on each and every dress I had in my closet. The three-hour gap I had between the invitation and lunch I spent in front of the mirror deciding which outfit, shoes, makeup, and hairstyle would fit me the best, and my effort was well worth it.

"You look wonderful," was the first thing Richard said to me when we met. "I like your hair straight like this," he said, looking at me carefully. "You always wear wavy hair, and it's good, but straight looks even better." "Thanks," I said, smiling. His reaction was exactly what I'd aimed for. "You smell different, too," he said. "Your perfume is different. I like it." Richard couldn't stop complimenting my appearance, from my dress to the slightest details of my earrings. "How have you been? You look terrific, so I assume you feel good too," he said to me on our way to the restaurant. "I've been good, thank you," I answered briskly. "Have you been seeing anyone?" he finally asked, revealing what he really had on his mind. "Not really, you?" "No." He stopped. "Who was that fat ugly guy at Skybar you left with?" "What?" I chuckled. I knew he meant Alex, but he wasn't fat or ugly. "He wasn't ugly," I said, giggling. "He was short and ugly. I remember," Richard disagreed. "He actually looked a lot like you," I teased him. "Chloe and I thought for a second it was one of your cousins." I giggled, and Richard only looked at me, raising his eyebrow. "Speaking of fat and ugly," I started, "who were those three ridiculously tacky Ohio-looking girls you left with?" "Ohio-looking?" He started laughing. "Those were Nate's friends. We all went together to the after-party," he explained, unable to contain a smile. He always liked when I got jealous. "So, Chloe tells me you enjoyed your dates with Ursula," I said, perfectly aware that I was playing with fire. "Chloe likes to interfere, doesn't she?" he said, irritated. "You have always treated her bad, but it's not about her this time." "We had a relationship, you and I, and she decided it was her place to interfere and ruin everything," he said angrily. "She didn't ruin anything," I disagreed, "we did, you and I. Well, you mostly," I teased, but he didn't react. "Did you get scared when I said I never want to see you again?" I continued teasing. "Yes," he said softly, "yes, I did." I didn't expect to hear something like that, an honest answer. "All the others, those girls . . . they come and go, they don't mean anything, just faces." He turned to me. "You are different. You would always mean a lot to me, even if we were not together. There will always be a special place for you in my heart." The sentiment caught me off guard. With that one sentence, he managed to describe everything I had in my heart.

Richard took me to my favorite place in town, Water Grill in Santa Monica. Eating lobster and shrimp cocktail for lunch, I couldn't stop thinking how grateful I was we were there. After all, there are men out there who take you to eat tacos out of a greasy old food cart. We laughed and teased each other a lot, just like in those first weeks two and a half years ago when we had just started dating, and it was the best date I'd had in many, many months.

"What do you wanna do next?" Richard asked as we left the restaurant and were walking to the valet. "I . . . I don't know," I said, "let's take it slow this time, OK?" "Sure, whatever you say," he agreed.

An hour later, I was in his bed, taking it fast . . . just how we both liked it.

XXIII

ODI ET AMO

"I hate, and I love." I think Catullus was on to something, and a person really can have those conflicting feelings at the same time. I, for one, have experienced it.

Even though Richard and I were together once again, we were in a very uncertain phase. I just tried to enjoy the moment to the fullest. After all, with Richard and me, it never lasted. But this time around, our relationship was very different. We were spending a lot of time together, just as before, but we only seemed to adore and appreciate each other's company on the weekdays; on the weekends, however, we were singles again. We never discussed this. It just happened on its own. And perhaps it was even beneficial for us. It all started when one Friday Chloe and I went out to the White party, and I just decided not to tell Richard.

"Oh, God! Look," Chloe said as loud as she

could, trying to out-scream the music, "it's Richard!" She pointed with her finger across the room. At that moment, I felt glued to the spot, unable to move. I began mentally preparing to break up again. "You think he noticed us?" I asked nervously. "Definitely," she said as we witnessed how Richard tried to make his way to us from the other side of the club. "Hello, hello," he said, chuckling and coming closer to us. "Hi." I was nervous, and it made my voice sound weird. "What are you doing here?" he asked, sipping his gin and tonic. "Same as you, I guess." I tried to calm down, realizing that very conveniently, Richard had also forgotten to mention that he was going to the party. "I'm here with my friend. We are going to the private room," he said casually, without extending an invitation... Richard had this superpower; he could drink as much as he liked and still not appear drunk, at least to most people. Unfortunately, that superpower of his didn't work on me. I could tell the alcohol level in his body in less than a minute, and that time he was completely wasted. "We want to go to the room too," I said, looking first at Chloe and then turning to Richard. "I'll get you in, but not her!" It wasn't my first rodeo, and I had already heard anything and everything he could possibly say, but that statement came as a shock. "That's a vulgar thing to say!" I said in outrage. "Come on." He wasn't giving up. "I don't want her there," he said, pointing at Chloe with his finger, "but you are always welcome."

"Richard, don't make it any worse than it already is." At that moment, I was grateful to Chloe for being an adult and not causing a scene. "Let's go!" I told her, turning my back on Richard. We didn't see him for the rest of the night, and even though his behavior toward Chloe had been less than ideal, I decided to let it go. He was obviously doing lots of cocaine that night and probably wouldn't even remember any of it. Plus, thanks to what happened, I got the chance to spend the night just as I wanted to, flirting and dancing with a bunch of different guys.

"Hi," I heard Richard say as he answered the phone the next morning. "I'm about to die," he whispered painfully, and jokes aside, he did sound as if he was dying there. "I'm not feeling so good myself," I admitted. "What happened last night?" "What do you mean?" I asked, not knowing exactly what he was referring to. "I thought I saw you last night, but I don't really remember anything." Just as I suspected. "Did we get in a fight? I woke up having a feeling that I told you something, so I'm just calling to apologize, just in case . . ." I chuckled, unable to control myself. "You really don't remember, huh?" I paused. "You were so rude to Chloe, and to me, too, actually." "I was?" he asked, surprised. "I'm sorry for anything I said to you. I don't remember a thing." Richard apologizing? It was a nice improvement. "Come over," he asked, "so we can hangover together?" I giggled. "Yes, we will suffer together and cuddle and then get some unhealthy fast food to feel better. It will be a dream." "Well, how can I refuse such an offer?" I giggled again.

That Saturday afternoon, we did everything

Richard described. We slept, ate junk food, and even threw up together . . . and later when we both felt better, we went out and about again. The next week it happened again, and the week after it, until it became a sort of tradition. At first, I liked it, but little by little, and not without the influence of my friends, I started to think it was suspicious and that probably Richard was cheating on me again. We all know what they say: "Once a cheater, always a cheater." I mentioned my worries to Richard once, but he only laughed, reassuring me nothing was going on and that I had nothing to worry about. The reassurance wasn't very reassuring, but it was obvious he liked the way things were and had no desire to make any changes, so for the sake of both of us, I went with it, at least for one more week.

"Candice and I are going to Delilah tonight. You should come with us!" Chloe told me as the three of us were having brunch on Saturday morning. Candice was a girl I knew from school and who somehow became very close friends with Chloe after the three of us went to that LA fashion show. "Yes! You have to come," Candice demanded, "you never go out with me anymore." The truth was that I didn't really enjoy going out with her. She was a nice girl, but the bars she used to hang out at were just horrible places. To be honest, I was surprised how Chloe managed to convince her to give Delilah a chance. I knew she hated places like that just as much as I hated cheap bars. "I don't really have plans, so why not," I agreed. We decided not to get too dressed up, not to drink much, and not to stay up late.

"This is what you call 'not dressed up'?" Chloe said sarcastically as I got into her car. "What? It's a casual dress," I said. "I knew you would wear a dress," Candice said, for some reason very joyfully. "It's a CASUAL dress," I repeated, irritated. "Your boobs are all out!" Candice laughed. "That's the whole point," Chloe remarked bitterly, and we all burst out laughing.

Delilah was so dull that evening—disappointed, we stayed only thirty minutes then left.

We checked out almost half a dozen places in West Hollywood, but everything was dead. "Where are all the people?" Chloe asked the security guy at the entrance of Laurel Hardware. "There is a big party at Skybar tonight," he said, "I guess everyone went there."

"We have to go to Skybar," I told my girls in my usual bossy manner as we sat at the half-empty bar. "No!" Chloe refused. "Why not?" I didn't expect a refusal. "Tell me, was there any time we went to Skybar and it didn't end badly?" she said, lifting an eyebrow. "The time I met Richard!" "My point exactly," she said sarcastically. "Hey! Now you are just being mean!" I said, sipping melted ice from the bottom of my glass. "I don't mind going to Skybar," Candice said quietly, interfering with our teasing. "Perfect!" I exhaled. "We voted and majority rules. God bless democracy,"

I said, raising my glass and giggling.

The security guy was right, and it seemed everyone we knew was at Skybar that night. "We're definitely going to meet someone we know tonight," I said to Chloe excitedly as we desperately tried to make our way through the crowd. "That's practically why I wasn't a fan of the idea to come here. I want to meet new people, not someone we already know," she said, pushing some guy out of her way. "Sophie!" I heard a familiar voice say. I turned around and saw Richard. Everyone we knew really was there that night. "Oh," was the only sound I made. "Hi," he said, coming closer and giving me a kiss. "Chloe, hi," he said politely, turning to her. "Hello, I'm Richard, nice to meet you," he continued, seeing a new face among our crowd. "Oh, sorry, this is my friend Candice. Candice, this is Richard, my . . ." I paused, not knowing what exactly he was to me. "Her boyfriend," Richard finished the sentence and looked at me smiling. "It's very nice to meet you," Candice said, shaking his hand. "I didn't know you were coming here," I said, taking Richard's hand and leading him away from the girls. "I didn't know you were going to be here either, but here we are." "Who are you here with?" I asked him suspiciously. "My friends, who else could I be here with? A mistress?" he chuckled, but to me, it was no joke. "Go back to your girls, and you can join me later. Deal?" I nodded. "Ladies," he announced loudly so both Chloe and Candice could hear him, "I have a tab at the bar upstairs. All drinks are on me." Then he turned to me. "Just tell them my last name at the bar and get whatever you want." He smiled, kissed my cheek, and with that, he was gone. "You are an adorable couple," Candice said to me when he left. "Thank you." "That's the reason you wanted to come here, isn't it," Chloe asked me in irritation. "No!" I rebelled, "I had no idea Richard was going to be here." She didn't believe me, and it was all written all over her face, but, surprisingly, she let it go.

When I arrived at Skybar, I was already tipsy. Another couple of drinks, and I was barely standing on my feet. While Chloe was flirting with some hot Italian guy, I decided to wander around. "Come on, Candice, let's go!" I grabbed her hand and pulled her along to follow me. "Where are we going?" she asked. "Just around. To see people, and then we'll stop by the bar. I'm out of alcohol." Thirty minutes and one crazy-ass cocktail later, I was not only unable to stay straight but unable to even think or talk straight. "My love!" I yelled, seeing Richard coming my way. "Hey babe," he said, getting the glass out of my hand, "how many of these have you had?" "I don't know. Not too many," I said, trying to act normal but very unsuccessfully. He turned to the bartender, and I heard him saying something like, "don't serve her any more drinks, please." "Can I have my glass back?" I said, trying to reach for it. "Sophie, Sophie!" He sounded serious. "I know you, and you have had enough. Let's get you some water, and we'll leave soon, OK?"

It wasn't OK with me at all. I had no intention to leave. "We?" I asked. "We are leaving together?"

"Yes, of course, we are leaving together. Someone has to take care of you. You are obviously too drunk to do it yourself." "Candice, if you wanna leave, you can go back to Chloe," I said, putting my arms around Richard. "My man is going to take care of me." I giggled with this stupid drunk giggle I have. "Are you sure?" Candice asked carefully. "Don't worry, I'll take her home," Richard reassured her. He regretted his decision less than ten minutes later when I wouldn't leave him alone, not even for a moment. There are different types of drunk—mine is a mischievous five-year-old baby, and I usually get on the nerves of anyone and everyone around. Plus, it's extremely hard to make me do anything I don't want to, and I do not really want to do anything except drink more alcohol. "Would you please sit on a couch for a second and drink your water," Richard said desperately, trying to calm me down. I sat down and started sipping the water he gave me, only to see him talking to some other girl. In a second, I rushed from the spot and jumped at him. "Who is this?" I asked. My face was getting all red in anger, like in those old Disney cartoons. "This is Sonia," Richard said with a nervous smile. "Does Sonia know you have a girlfriend?" I asked loudly and looked at her. "Excuse us!" he said politely and dragged me back to the couch. "This is my colleague's wife! Don't embarrass me!" he said, pushing me down to sit. "Fine." I should've felt sorry, but I didn't. "We are going home soon. Please just give me thirty minutes to say goodbyes."

I agreed to that, and I really meant it. In fact,

I blame the mess that happened that night on the next ten minutes, when I saw a guy I knew through Mia. "Kevin!" I screamed, waving at him. "Sophie, hi." He looked very happy to see me. "Hi, it's been a long time," I said, giving him a hug. "How's Mia? You still see her?" "Of course I see her, she is my friend." I smiled. "And she is doing great, by the way." "Good, I'm glad to hear it." After a short greeting and small talk, he got back to his group, and I got back to bothering Richard. "What did he want?" he asked in displeasure, pointing at Kevin. "He and Mia used to go out. He just said hi," I explained. "OK, everyone is leaving. Let's go." We started to walk toward the exit, but for every step we took, Richard seemed to find ten more people to say goodbye to, and most all of them were girls. I waited and waited for him, and I got tired of waiting. He was flirting with every girl at Skybar, and for everyone, he had an excuse—a colleague's wife, a girlfriend of a friend, a cousin, a client. I got so mad looking at it. Those girls had the same effect on me as a muleta on a bull. I stormed outside all mad and emotional and started to try to order myself an Uber, but it was already almost 2:00 a.m., which meant it would be impossible to get a ride. "Hey," I heard a male voice say. Raising my eyes from my phone, I saw Kevin. "Hey," I said without any enthusiasm. "Are you going to an after-party?" he asked me. "After-party? I didn't know there was one," I said, barely listening to what he was saying. At the moment my phone had all my attention. "Yes, everyone is going to Richard's house." "What? Richard Corbin's house?" I asked, to make sure we were talking about the same person. "Yeah, you know him?" I sniffed. "I do," I said, putting my phone away. "How do you know him?" I wondered. "Oh, I don't really . . . well, I know his brother." That was just music to my ears. Why, in a city with a population of four million people, did we still manage to know, date, and hook up with the same group?

I noticed Richard coming out of the club with a bunch of girls around him. It was as if he had totally forgotten I was there. Well, if that was what he wanted, that was what he would get. "Let's have our own after-party," I said to Kevin, flirting. "Our own?" He smiled, clearly enjoying the idea. "Yes, why go to Richard's party with a bunch of people there when we can have a private and intimate party with just a small group." I smiled, batting my eyelashes most coquettishly. "Yes! I love the idea." He called over his friends to tell them about the plan. They seemed even more excited than Kevin. "Let's go to my place Downtown," one guy, whose name I don't really remember, offered. He was very tall, with a full head of brown curly hair. For me, good hair is probably the most important feature in a man, even more important than height, I guess, and that guy had it all. "I'm down for it," I giggled, and as I did, I felt someone's hard stare. It's Richard, I thought to myself, it's got to be. I turned around. He was looking at me with a very careful gaze, almost as if he was studying me, trying to understand what my next move would be. I bet he didn't expect what happened next. A new Range Rover with a bunch of guys inside pulled over, and I jumped in it. I knew Richard was witnessing that little scene I played for him, and I knew he was pissed. Unfortunately, I didn't realize how much harm pissing him off would do to me.

"Can I play my music?" was the first thing I asked when we got to DTLA. "Sure," the cute guy said. His apartment was gorgeous—panoramic view of downtown LA, high ceilings, white furniture. It was a dreamland. I drank another glass of vodka cranberry, did two lines, and ten minutes later started talking about my favorite topic. "I mean, I love him, and I know he loves me, but maybe we're just not meant to be together. But it doesn't change the fact that he is the love of my life. You know what I mean?" I said to Kevin, and by the expression on his face at that moment, it was clear to me he had no idea what I was talking about nor any desire to know. "I feel sorry for you," he said. "Why?" I didn't feel sorry for myself, so why on earth would he. "I've heard of Richard, and he's not exactly a present." That statement pissed me off, and the cocaine I did wasn't helping me keep my anger in check. "Don't say that! Never say shit like that about Richard! Only I can talk shit about him. He is my boyfriend." It didn't make much sense, but for his own sake, Kevin agreed. In all that, I forgot the way I left Richard, but he didn't forget about me apparently. "Shit!" I said, seeing his name pop up on my phone. "What happened?" Kevin asked in concern as he finished another line. "Richard. He is calling me." "Don't answer," I heard the cute guy saying from the kitchen, "and don't give him my address. I don't want your crazy boyfriend to come and kill us all."

The problem was they didn't know my "crazy" boyfriend like I did. When he starts calling you, he won't stop until you answer. He called me eleven times, and then I got a text. 'You kidding me?' and then another, 'who did you go with?' 'I saw you leaving with him.' He called three more times. 'Pick up!' he texted when I chose to ignore him. 'I'll show you this time!' 'Don't do that!' and then he called again, and again, and again. "He still calling you?" Kevin asked. I nodded. "That's because his after-party got canceled," another guy, who wasn't there before, said. "I'm sorry, you are?" I asked in confusion, not remembering having seen him before. Apparently, I was so into reading all the crazy texts from Richard on my phone that I hadn't noticed that more people were coming into the place. "They are all coming from Richard's place here. The party got canceled," Kevin explained. 'Sophie, please pick up,' 'you are drunk,' 'PICK UP,' 'don't fuck anyone,' 'you will regret it tomorrow.' The texts just kept coming, and then the door opened, and I saw those same girls Richard had been flirting with outside Skybar. "Hey!" one of them said to me. "Hi." I tried to smile. "You were with Richard, right?" they asked me, and I didn't know why that question popped up or how I should answer.

"I was. Why?"

"Oh, we just left his place. Could you please not tell him that we came here?" "Sure," I said and walked away from them. What was all that about? Why would they want to keep it a secret? What exactly was happening at that place in Bel Air?

While I was in my thoughts, he called again, and this time I picked up. "What do you want?" I said in irritation. "Where are you?" he asked, ignoring my question. I sneaked to the balcony to avoid anyone overhearing me. "I'm in DTLA with those girls you tried to fuck," I accused him. "Kid, I don't try. If I want, I do it," he said arrogantly. "Anyway, get your things and come here." "Right," I sniffed. "Come on, you are drunk. You don't want to do it." He was trying to be convincing. "You left me there! And went on flirting with girls!" I yelled. "Please, come here, and we will talk about it." "Fine!" I said, knowing perfectly well that the choice was never mine. If I didn't come over, he would call and text me for the rest of the night. 'Get me an Uber to this address.' I texted him an address and went inside to make an excuse and leave. "I'm so sorry, but I have to go," I said to Kevin. "No! Are you going to Richard?" he asked me straight, and I was a little surprised by his boldness. "I'm going home," I lied with a straight face. "I have to wake up early tomorrow." "OK, I'll walk you to the elevator." I got my shoes, found my purse, and said bye to everyone right in time for Richard's text saying the car was downstairs. "Can I have your number?" Kevin asked as we waited for the elevator. "My number?" I chuckled. "What for?" "For calling you," he said, teasing. "Fine, you can. Write it down." I dictated my phone number to him, hugged him, and jumped into the elevator.

"Are you in the car?" Richard called the second I sat down in the white Toyota Prius and asked. "I am. I'll see you in a bit." I was about to hang up. "Wait!" Richard said, "who did you go to DTLA with? That guy Kevin?" "Yes," I answered shortly. "I thought you wanted to talk when I get to your place, or was it just an excuse to get me out of the apartment?" I asked, irritated. "It wasn't an excuse. I'll see you soon."

'Hey, this is Kevin, save my number.' I saw it on my screen when I hung up. 'It was so great seeing you tonight, I wish you would have stayed longer.' 'It was nice seeing you too,' I texted back. 'Why did you have to go home?' 'I told you, I have an early morning.' 'Maybe I can come over to your place?' For a moment, I didn't know how to react. 'What for?' I texted him. 'To keep each other company.' I was on thin ice, and it was cracking under my feet. 'I don't think Richard would be happy with that, and I wouldn't want to ruin my relationship with him,' I texted back. 'Some other time then? I would love to take you out on a date.' 'Sure.' We were texting each other back and forth for the next thirty minutes, right until I made it to Richard's house.

"Hola," I said, walking in. I was still under the effect of cocaine. "Senor, ¿Cómo estás?" I giggled, but Richard wasn't on the same page as me. "How much did you drink?" he asked judgmentally. "You are not the one to ask questions here!" I snapped. "You left me, went with some bitches, and after they didn't want to have sex with you, by some miracle, you remembered me." I sounded drunk, but I meant every word. "Did you do coke?" he asked, ignoring everything I was saying. "Not like it's any of your business, but yes, yes I did," I said with some unusual arrogance. "I knew it! Whenever you do it, you become very aggressive." "I'm aggressive because you ditched me at Skybar and went to flirt with a bunch of whores!" He didn't ignore it this time. "Yes, and where did you go? And who did you go with? That Kevin guy, who you assured me, was dating one of your friends. How very convenient!" He raised his voice and was almost yelling now. "The second I turned away, you jumped in a car with three men and went to their place doing God knows what! You do it every time! Every time you get drunk, you go out there trying to fuck everyone!" he yelled at me, and I'm not going to lie, I got a little scared seeing him like that. "I didn't fuck anyone, and I wasn't planning to," I said calmly, hoping to calm him down as well. "I went with them because I got mad at you, but I wasn't going to have sex with Kevin or anyone else." "Right," he chuckled sarcastically. At least he was no longer yelling, and as this thought crossed my mind, my phone vibrated, and an incoming text appeared. I reached for it, unlocked it, and was about to read the text when out of nowhere, Richard grabbed it out of my hands. "No!" I screamed in panic. "Give it back! Give it back to me!" My blood froze. My mind was going over everything I had on my phone, all the DMs on Instagram, all the texts, and the pics. "Give it back to me!" I yelled, desperately trying to reach for the phone, but every time Richard would manage to get away. I was jumping on him, pushing him, even digging my nails into him, but it was all in vain. Richard had already gone through half of my conversation with Kevin. "Give it back!" I kept on yelling, "give me my phone back!" "Stop it!" he screamed back at me and pushed me away. The force was too much for my body to handle. I lost my balance and fell on the floor, but instead of helping me up and apologizing, Richard walked into the living room with my phone still in possession. After a minute of regaining my consciousness, I managed to finally get up and rush into the living room after him. "You are a bitch!" he yelled the second he saw me. "Give it back, now!" I screamed hysterically and so loud that I'm sure half of the neighborhood heard me. "Don't you raise your voice at me!" he yelled with rage. I had never seen him like that before. It was a terrifying scene, and I had absolutely no idea what he was capable of. He looked at me, and I felt chills run through my whole body. "I will kill him!" he yelled and ran upstairs.

I was scared to death. In fact, death was the only thing on my mind at that moment. Mentally I was preparing myself to fall victim to domestic violence. I heard his footsteps. He was coming down the stairs. In ten seconds, he was back in the living room, holding car keys in his hand. "I swear to God, I'll kill that motherfucker!" In two big strides, he was already by the door, and I knew exactly where he was going. "Stop!" I screamed, rushing toward him and jumping in front of the door, trying to block his way out.

"Move!" he commanded me, but I didn't react. "I said move!" he said again, raising his voice this time. "Where are you going? What are you going to do, huh? He didn't do anything, and neither did I! Stop this madness, or someone will get hurt," I said with my voice shaking. "Move the fuck away!" he yelled and pushed me again, this time even harder. I fell on the floor and managed to land straight on my left hand, on which I wore a huge ring on my middle finger. First, I felt excruciating pain, then when I tried to get up, I noticed a drop of blood on the floor, my blood. I sat on the floor, touching my face. My bottom lip was cut right in the middle. Looking up, I saw Richard frozen there in fear and horror. "Sophie . . ." he whispered. I burst into tears. "I hate you!" I yelled. "I hate you!" He tried to help me get up, but I pushed him away. "Don't touch! Don't ever touch me again! I hate you! I don't want to see you!" I screamed, crying. "I'm sorry. I'm so sorry." It was all he could say at that moment. It seemed he was even more scared of himself than I was.

"My lip is going to bruise," I cried, "I will look horrible." I was hysterical, and the cocaine I did earlier only worsened the effect. "No, there won't be a bruise," he said, trying to calm me down. "I'll get you some ice, and there won't be any bruising." He rushed to the kitchen while I was on the floor crying so hard it was difficult for me to breathe. "I'll look horrible. I will look so horrible," I kept on repeating. "Here,"

Richard said, handing me a napkin full of ice. "I hate you! I want to go home!" I screamed.

"Stop yelling so much. Someone will call the police on us."

"Let them!" I screamed, unable to control myself. "Let the police come. They will arrest you! And you deserve it for beating me up!" He wanted to object but decided it was not the right moment. "OK, let's get you upstairs," he said, lifting me off the floor. "Don't touch me!" I screamed. "I hate you! I never hated anyone this much!" "That's fine," he said calmly, "you can hate me, but please let me get you into bed. You need to calm down." Despite all of his efforts, I was nowhere near calming down. I was having a panic attack. I couldn't stop crying. "Let me go home! I want to go home!" I screamed at him. "You will. I will get you home, but you need to calm down first." He lifted me up and carried to the bedroom. I was still hysterically crying my guts out. "OK, come on, let's wash you up." He washed my face, brushed my hair, changed me from a dress into one of my PJ's I had at his place, and carried me to bed. "I'll sleep in the other room," he said and was about to leave. "No!" I said through my crying. "Don't leave me!"

He lay down next to me, putting his arms around me. That night I cried until the pillow was all wet, until there were no more tears left in my eyes. At seven in the morning, I finally fell asleep, exhausted and scared, wishing I had never met Richard.

XXIV

A TIME FOR EVERYTHING

It took more than a week for my lip to get back to its natural pink color, and by the end of that week, not only had I fully forgiven Richard, but I had also convinced myself that the whole incident was entirely my fault. Richard didn't seem to have any objections there, and instead of talking it out, we both pretended the night never happened. After all, denial was kind of our specialty.

"Let's go out tonight," Richard suggested when we talked on the phone. "It's Friday the thirteenth," I said, and for someone who knew me, that statement should have been more than enough. "You don't really believe it, do you?" he asked, sniffing with arrogance. "I do, actually, and you know that!" I replied. "Nothing is going to happen," he assured me. "We will have dinner and go home." I chose to trust him, even though I had a weird feeling, impossible to explain. On some subconscious level, I felt something bad was going to happen that night.

"You are not even ready?" I complained, seeing Richard still in his shower robe when I walked in. "I thought we had reservations at nine." "I canceled it," he said, lying on the couch with his phone. "I would really appreciate a heads up." Not being a fan of the whole going-out-on-Friday-the-thirteenth idea, I was relieved he had come to his senses and decided to stay home, but after spending two hours getting ready just to stay home, it seemed a bit hurtful. "Why did you change your mind?" I asked. "I didn't," he said shortly, staring at his phone and paying absolutely no attention to me. "Hey!" I walked to him, snapping my fingers in front of his face. "You made me get ready when I didn't want to go out in the first place, and now you are lying here not talking and texting someone," I said, annoyed. "I'm texting my friend." He didn't even care about a single thing I said. "Cool, I'm going home!" I grabbed my little purse from the counter and headed to the door. "Come on! I'm sorry, I was just texting my friend. He is on his way from OC. We'll wait for him and go out all together." That was not what I wanted to hear and not something I was willing to do on a Friday night.

"I thought it was going to be just the two of us."

"Yes, but then he asked me to hang, and since I made plans with you, I told him to come along," Richard explained.

"And you didn't think to even ask me?" I was pissed and couldn't hide it. "If I knew, I wouldn't have come."

"You always complain I don't go out with you, and now I'm going out with you, and you are not happy again," Richard said, raising his voice. "Don't raise your voice!" I snapped. "When I talked about going out more, I meant you and me, together as a couple, not with some friend of yours whose name I have never heard before."

"His name is Alan," Richard pointed out. "I don't care! You don't listen to what I'm saying!" "Because you are not saying anything. You are getting angry with me and want to fight. Are you on your period?" If I was angry before, that phrase made me just furious. "You know what, go on your date with Alan, Richard!" I turned around and stormed out. "I'm sorry," I heard him say as I neared the front gate. "I'm sorry! Can you come back inside? I don't want it to be a recap of the last week." Neither did I, so I followed him back into the house.

His friend was about thirty minutes away, and Richard went upstairs to get ready while I sat in the living room, pouring myself a drink and turning on the sound system. I was already tipsy when the doorbell rang. "Hi." A very cute, tall guy appeared in front of me. "You must be Sophie. I'm Alan." He was a 27-year-old very handsome and polite law-school student. "Hey! Come on in," I said, feeling like the lady of the house at that moment, "Richard is almost ready. Do you want anything to drink?"

"Oh, thank you, I'm good."

"You sure? I'm a pretty talented bartender. Though I only know two drinks, I'm extremely good at making them." He laughed, refusing politely. "So, how do you know Richard?" I asked him, trying to avoid an awkward silence. "We only just met a couple of months ago, to be honest, through a mutual friend." I was dying to know who that mutual friend was afraid it might happen to be someone I'd slept within the past, so I decided not to ask. "And you two?" he asked. "How long have you guys been together?" The fact that Richard didn't mention anything about our relationship felt very offensive. "We have been together over two years now . . . back and forth," I chuckled nervously. "Oh, wow! I didn't realize you have known each other for so long." He sounded surprised. "Richard told me he was seeing someone but never went into details." Seeing? Is that what we were doing here? "Seeing" each other?

On the one hand, it was understandable he hadn't shared a lot with this guy he'd just met. And on the other, it was weird that the subject of his relationship with me never had been brought up. Although I was hurt and mad at Richard, I chose not to show my true feelings and only smiled when the insult was thrown in my face. "There you guys are," I heard Richard say. "You two have hit it off?" I wanted to say that not only had we hit it off I'd also discovered an unpleasant truth, but instead, I only smiled and said, "Yes, your friend Alan is great."

"Perfect!" Richard patted him on the shoulder. "Should we do some shots before we head out?" To my big surprise, Alan was more than excited to drink with Richard. What a weird guy, I thought to myself as I followed them to the kitchen to have a shot of tequila.

At dinner, the guys did all the talking, and I was mostly left out of any discussion, and even though Alan was the third wheel, that night He and Richard made me feel like one. I had no idea what I was doing there, and it made me angry, which led to my drinking one too many glasses of alcohol. "You should slow down," was the first thing Richard said to me during the whole of dinner. "I'm fine, thanks for the concern," I said acidly. We finished dinner, and when I thought we could finally be done with that unpleasant evening and I could go home and start a scandal, Richard decided we had to go to Tao. Although I hated the idea, no one cared, and once again, I had absolutely no say in it whatsoever. First we went to Tao, and then he decided to check out Beauty and Essex, and then finally he dragged us to Highlight Room. I loved the place; it was the company I despised that night. "We should find Alan some girl," Richard said enthusiastically. "I don't feel like a matchmaker," I told him in annoyance. As long as Richard was sober, he was still hanging with me, without any enthusiasm, but at least he wasn't leaving me all alone in a club. The second he got a little tipsy, that changed completely. In fact, all it took was for me to go to the bathroom, and the moment I was back, he and Alan were both gone. Just great! I was mad at him but not surprised. Despite my desire to leave, I decided to wander around. My ego was hurt, and I needed something or someone to heal it. It wasn't the first time Richard had done something similar to me, and I didn't know why I was still tolerating this behavior.

"Hey," I heard a voice say, bringing me back from my thoughts to reality. "Hi." I smiled uncontrollably. Two tall, very handsome guys were looking at me. "Would you like to join us?" one of them asked. "Oh, I . . ." I tried to find a reason why I shouldn't, but I couldn't find any. They were both very attractive, but the one who invited me looked like a Greek god. "What would you like to drink?" "Champagne, please." He called the waitress over to get me a glass. "I'm Chris. This is my friend Tony." He pointed to the guy behind him. "I'm Sophie." "Are you here by yourself, Sophie?" he asked, concerned, and since the situation I was in wasn't very flattering, I simply replied that I was with friends and I couldn't find them in the crowd. He was satisfied with the answer and invited me to come to an after-party with the two of them. At that moment, I regretted ever being in a relationship, and my mind was in a debate with itself. On the one hand, I had a boyfriend, yet on the other, he was somewhere missing, and it was his choice to get lost. So did that mean that acceptance would be permissible? "Thank you, but I really can't." Those were the hardest words that had ever come out of my mouth. I finished my glass of champagne, apologized, and then left. 'Where are you?' was the text Richard had sent me almost an hour after we split up, and after texting each other back and forth, I was accused of leaving. 'I'm still at the bar,' he texted me, and being outraged by the whole situation, I headed there to let him know what I thought about his behavior and the disrespect and rudeness he had shown me that evening. All I found at the bar, though, was a disappointment. Richard was surrounded by four women he was flirting with, buying them drinks and sharing cocaine. Without even calling him out on it, I left. The evening had brought me only distress, and it was time for me to stop the torture and go home.

Going home was my original plan, but when I got in the Uber, I felt an extreme need to party. Too bad I hadn't exchanged numbers with the hot guy from the club. Luckily, I still had some friends, and after texting into a group chat, I got an invitation to a huge party that was happening in The Valley. I stopped by at home, changed, and was on my way to Studio City. 'Where did you go??' Richard texted me when I was already halfway through Coldwater Canyon. Probably the girls had left him, or maybe the club was closing, and he remembered he had come with someone. In any case, I chose to ignore him. 'You went with a guy?' he texted. 'If you cheat on me, I will never forgive you.' Outraged by this assumption, I texted back, 'I'm never gonna do that, you know why, cause unlike you, I'm not interested in other people.' "Where are you?" he asked when I answered his third phone call. "On my way to a friend's house," I said calmly. "You were with a bunch of girls, and I decided it was a reason enough for me to leave." "What are you talking about?" He was drunk and probably high on cocaine, and I knew the conversation wasn't going to end well. "I'm outside the club. Come back!" "I'm on my way to my friend's! But you go have fun." Weirdly, I didn't much care what he was going to do or whom he was going to do it with, but he kept calling me and asking to go to his place. "I'm in The Valley," I said, annoyed, "if you wanted me to come home with you, you should have thought about it before you decided to get yourself a harem." I was adamant, but after ten more phone calls, I gave in, deciding it was easier to do what he was asking and go to Bel Air.

"I'm going to go see my friends for thirty minutes or so, and then you can call me an Uber." He agreed to those terms. It was almost three in the morning when I finally made it to The Valley. I came, I saw, I said hi to everyone, and I was ready to leave. I texted Richard, letting him know I was ready for an Uber. Fifteen minutes passed with no response. Maybe he found some other chick to go home with, or maybe he changed his mind and went to some after-party. Anyway, the thought of him ditching me again pissed me off majorly, so there was nothing left but to call and yell at him. I called once, he didn't answer. Twice, no answer again. The third time I heard a voice on the other line, but it wasn't Richard. "Who's this?" I asked, confused. "It's Alan. Richard can't talk right now." "What?" I went from confused to mad in a second. "What do you mean he can't talk? Put him on the phone!" "Sophie, he is not in the state to talk right now. He isn't feeling well, just . . . just go home, and you call him tomorrow." After that, he just hung up on me. I tried to call again, but no one was answering. Probably he got too drunk. And with this thought and an undisturbed conscience, my after-party began.

When I woke up the next morning, I saw three texts from Richard that he had sent to me at five in the morning. 'So you left me like this.' 'Thanks.' 'Enjoy whatever you are doing.' I didn't know what to think. I started calling him, but he was still not answering the phone. I called four times, worrying that something might have happened the night before, but after a while, I convinced myself that I was probably overreacting to a drunk text. After all, how many times had something similar happened before? It was just a bad hangover at worst, and he was going to call me back when he woke up. Just like that, I tranquilized my conscience again.

When he didn't call back at noon, I texted him, 'Is everything OK??' but didn't hear back. And when at 2:00 p.m. he was still MIA, I became worried sick. "I don't know what to do," I said in desperation to Chloe over the phone. "I called some of his friends I know, and no one has seen or heard from him." "Maybe he is still asleep," she suggested. "I thought about it, but it's already 3:00 p.m. Have you ever been so hungover you slept all day without waking up or checking your phone even once?" "No . . . but maybe he has." Maybe she was right, and I was making a big deal out of it, but this weird sensation was telling me something was not right. "Hold on. I think I found this guy Alan's Insta. Should I text him?" I asked indecisively. "I mean, if it makes your anxiety go away, I don't see why not." And with Chloe's permission, I started to compose a perfect text for Alan. After checking it ten times for the right spelling, I finally pressed send. Even though it was supposed to end my anxiety, it only increased it. I was nervously staring at my phone, waiting for a reply, which seemed to take him forever to send. Forty-five minutes later, I finally got a text. 'Hi Sophie, don't worry, Richard is in the hospital, but he is feeling better, I stayed with him all night and now one of his friends is here. Nothing to worry about." I read it over and over. Hospital? What?? 'Could you tell me what hospital please?' I texted back, but to my surprise, he avoided the question and just kept saying that everything was fine. I didn't understand what was happening, so I pressed him until he cracked and finally gave me a straight answer. 'Richard doesn't want anyone here.' 'But I'm not anyone.' 'Sophie, he doesn't want YOU here." And the cat was out of the bag. I meant so little. He didn't even want me there by his side. He didn't even care to tell me what was happening. My feelings meant nothing to him. 'OK, thanks.' That was all I could text back. I felt anxious like never before, imagining what my life without Richard would be like. Surely it would be easier without his presence in it, but it would be absolutely dull. He was this element that kept me going, and I didn't know how I would live without him.

The thought of losing him terrified me, and even if he didn't want to see me, all I really needed was to know that he was fine. 'Alan, I'm sorry to bother you, but please can you tell me what happened, why did Richard end up in the hospital, and how serious it was?' Even though he didn't want to give me many details, I'm sure he knew it was only right to let me know what happened. After all, I deserved that much.

Apparently, Richard got into a fight on the street, and it ended badly for everyone involved. He had been taken to the hospital, but now all that was already in the past. There was nothing life-threatening, and he would be out and about in two days. I always knew his arrogance would get him in big trouble one day, and look who was right. And all of that on Friday the thirteenth—and I was right about it, again. I tried to get the hospital's name out of Alan, but that was one thing he wasn't willing to share. As for me, I had nothing left to do but to wait, wait until Richard was out of the hospital, and then make peace with him and be there for him. That's what I did, and with my lack of patience, it wasn't easy, but I tried my best to stay calm, relaxed, and avoid any guilt trips.

The torture continued for two days, and on the third, I got a message from Richard—

'No, everything is not OK, thanks for leaving me.' Rage, I thought, reading it. Rage is good; it means he would get over it over time. But then the second text hit me. 'No worries, just let me know if you receive any letters for me. Appreciate it.' Now that was a bad sign. Indifference. There is nothing worse than indifference. 'What do you mean no worries, seriously? Like that? I was going crazy that something happened, called you all day nonstop, was so worried I texted your friend to find out you were in a hospital and I wasn't someone important enough to even know that, and it was very politely pointed out that you didn't want me there, and now you are acting like this, accusing me of something I didn't do, nice.' I texted back, unable to control all the frustration I had experienced in the past seventy-two hours, but all Richard did was leave me on "read." Whatever. If he didn't want to talk to me, I wouldn't pressure him. I kept my distance, giving him the time I assumed he needed.

"Sophie, you are never going to believe who just called me," was the first thing out of Chloe's mouth when I picked up the phone. "Kai!" she announced before I even had a chance to guess. "Why did he call you?" I was taken a bit by surprise. The last time I saw him was on Richard's birthday. "He asked about Richard." "What did he ask?" The longer we had this conversation, the more confused it got. "Richard doesn't answer his phone calls. In fact, he doesn't talk to anyone, and someone told Kai that Richard was with you the night everything happened."

"I get that, but why did he call you?"

"I don't know. He asked if you happened to talk to his brother and said he would call you later today."

I understood why Richard didn't want to talk to me, but why did he ignore everyone else, even his family? I decided I had to try calling him, and to my surprise, he picked up.

"Yes?" He sounded irritated.

"Hi," I said softly, hoping it would change his attitude toward me. "I was worried about you. Thought I'd give you a call, see how you're doing and if you needed anything."

"I'm OK" was his short answer.

"I heard you have been ignoring everyone."

"Where did you hear that?" he asked, and before I had a chance to give it any thought, my big mouth said, "From Kai." I regretted it that very second. Why didn't I think before I spoke? "You talked to my brother?" I could hear the notes of anger in his voice. "Yes . . . I mean, no, not really. Chloe spoke to him . . . he called her because he was worried about you," I mumbled. "OK, thanks for letting me know. I have to go." "Wait . . . I . . ." He hung up before I finished. It wasn't a good sign, but at least he answered my call. The thought that out of all the other people calling mine was the only one he answered was quite flattering, considering I was the one he was the maddest at. While my ego was complimented, my phone was ringing, and I saw an unknown phone number on my screen. "Hello?" I said, unsure. "Fifi." That voice I could recognize in a crowd of a thousand. "Hi, Kai," I sounded flirtatious, "how's your trip?" "Hey, I'm good. Listen," he said, going straight for the chase, "have you spoken to my brother lately? I'm trying to understand what happened and how bad things are."

"How bad things are. . ." For some reason, I thought there was nothing life-threatening or dangerous. "I have, but if you want to ask me what happened that night, I have to disappoint you. I wasn't there, and to be honest, I wasn't in the hospital, either."

"I don't know what to do. My flight to LA is not until next week, but if things are serious, I could fly in tonight and be there tomorrow morning. But he wouldn't even pick up my calls." He was worried, and it made me worried as well. What if I had underestimated the seriousness of the situation, and everything was way worse than I had thought? "Do you want me to go to his house and check on him?" The words just flew out of my mouth. "You would do that?" he asked with some surprise as if I didn't care about his brother at all. "Absolutely! Why wouldn't I?!"

"What if he's there with another girl?" I didn't even think of such a possibility. "Richard is not you!" I said bitterly, offended by the very idea of that scenario. "Of course he isn't," Kai said, chuckling. "Anyway, I will go there at once and call you after."

"Thank you, Fifi."

Without any hesitation or second thoughts, I jumped in my car and headed toward Bel Air. All the way there, my mind was revolving around what Kai had said to me. Was Richard humping someone right then? I tried to convince myself it was absurd, but it is always easier to put an idea into one's head than to take it out. Twenty-five minutes later, I was in front of the gates of Richard's house. I saw his car parked outside and decided it was a clear sign he was home, and with full confidence of success, I rang the bell. But to my surprise, no one answered. I rang again and again, and still no result. Frustrated, I started calling his cell, but Richard was canceling each and every one of my calls. He must be with another girl. Kai was right. 'I'm outside your house. Can you please open the door?' I texted, but there was no response. So I continued both calling his phone and ringing the doorbell. 'I'm not going to leave until you talk to me!' I texted him and meant it.

"What do you want?" Richard asked, annoyed, answering my call.

"I want to come in, obviously."

"I'm not home. I'm at the doctor's office right now."

"But your car is outside your house . . ."

"I took an Uber." Perhaps it was true. If he got in a fight, maybe his arm was broken or worse.

"I'll wait for you here."

"Why? What do you want?" It was an interesting question. "I want to check on you and see if everything is OK."

"Fine, you can come to the doctor's office if you want."

"I do. Text me the address." That was obviously not the response he was hoping for. The address he texted me was a 35-minute drive and seemed to be somewhere in The Valley.

'I'll be there in 35,' I texted him, got in my car, and started the ride.

It wasn't even a hospital, just some little medical building near a mall.

"Can I help you?" one of two female receptionists asked me as I walked in. "Yes, hi, my friend is with the doctor right now. Do you mind if I wait out here?" They seemed confused, and I didn't know what it was I did or said wrong. Then the same lady that greeted me gave me a pitying look. "The doctor is not in today." I guess I was looking like a betrayed wife because their expressions showed a lot of empathy and compassion for me. "Oh," was the only thing I managed to get out of myself, "perhaps it's a mix-up. Excuse me." I ran the hell out of the office, embarrassed and humiliated. Not to answer my phone calls was one thing, but Richard had just made me drive fifteen miles to some imaginary doctor's office he'd googled just to get rid of me. All I wanted to do was to be there for him, but apparently, he didn't need me, and even though my feelings were hurt, I made up my mind not to pressure him again, for, as I told myself, he needed to heal his wounds both figuratively and literally before he would be ready to see my face again, and there was no better healer than time. And if that was what he needed, that's what I would give him.

XXV

I JUST WANT ATTENTION

"You need to go out!" Chloe declared to me as we had lunch with a group of friends at Montage.

"I am out right now with you, am I not?"

"You are, honey, but what she meant was that you need to stop your denial and go get some," my friend Liam, who was also my free-of-charge therapist, said with his usual directness. "I don't need to get some," I disagreed. "Richard and I will get back together soon, as we always do." "Have you spoken to him?" Chloe asked. It was a question I wasn't willing to answer because the fact was I hadn't heard from Richard in weeks. I had thought at first that with time he would overcome his grudge, but time had passed, and he was still not ready to talk to me. As much as I hated to admit it, perhaps my friends were right. I needed to make peace with the fact that Richard and I were done for good, that perhaps that was the last straw. "Fine," I said, sighing, "I'll go out if it pleases you." "Oh, it does," Liam teased me.

That week I was dining out almost every night. My ego was flattered—at least five guys hit on me every evening—but as much as I enjoyed the attention, my heart was in a different place. I liked to talk to men, to flirt with them, to tease them a little, but I wouldn't even give them my phone number. No, I wasn't interested, and I wasn't ready to move on. I knew, or perhaps I hoped, that there was still a chance that Richard would forgive me and stop seeing me as the bad guy in that whole story. But the more time passed, the harder the reality hit me—the odds that Richard would ever talk to me again were miserably low. Chloe and Liam were right. I needed to stop my denial and face reality, and what better way than to find a date. The flaw in the plan was that I had absolutely no interest in any man except Richard.

"I can't believe you dragged me here again," I complained to Chloe as we walked through the door of Ysabel. "Oh, you love this place. Quit complaining." I did love that place, but somehow, ever since Richard stopped talking to me, everything felt different, and things I used to like and enjoy didn't bring me as much joy as before. "I have a good feeling about tonight," Chloe said optimistically, and although I didn't share that optimism, I could still get some pleasure out of the evening.

It was a full house that night—hundreds of handsome single guys, and also married guys pretending to be single for the night. We tried to find an empty spot to sit, but it was impossible. The place was so crowded that night we barely made it to the bar alive. It took us at least twenty minutes to get two glasses of champagne, and when we were making our way out of that pit called a bar, I felt someone's touch on my skin. I turned around, and in an instant, the evening elevated from dull to fabulous. "It's you," I said, losing control of what was coming out of my mouth. "Hey." It was the same guy I'd met at Highlight Room the night I got in a fight with Richard. What were the chances of running into him again, and especially now? Maybe the universe was saying something to me, and maybe it was saying it through him. "You left so fast the other night I didn't get a chance to even ask for your number." His smile brightened the room. I had never seen a person so beautiful, and somewhere deep down, I was flattered he was flirting with me.

"I'm Sophie."

"I remember." That smile was to die for. "Is she a friend of yours?" He pointed at Chloe, who was standing right behind me, sipping her champagne. "Oh, I'm sorry, this is Chloe," I said, introducing them. "It is very nice to meet you, Chloe, I'm Chris." Thank God he mentioned his name. I remembered his gorgeous face but had very little memory of his name, which wasn't something unusual, considering I couldn't remember Richard's name for the first two weeks we knew each other. "Are you here with a friend?" I asked him. "Yes, we're actually having a birthday dinner and then going to the hills for an after-party. You should join us."

"We wouldn't want to intrude on the birthday dinner, but after-party sounds great." Who needs to sit at the table with a bunch of strangers when we can go someplace intimate to drink and make out—cheers to those who invented after-parties. "No problem, give me your phone number, and I'll come to find you when we are about to leave." He was just perfect—handsome, tall, good manners, a great sense of style, something almost all of my exes were missing, and, more importantly, he seemed to like me just as much as I liked him. I could eat him up right then and there. There was this chemistry I hadn't felt with anyone except Kai, and yet this time, it was even stronger. I had this unreal desire for the man in front of me, a man I knew nothing about. He went back to his table, leaving me alone with my fantasies. "He is the hottest guy I had ever met," I claimed when we were a safe distance from him. "He is handsome, for sure," Chloe agreed. "We should walk by his table later and check out his friends. Maybe there is someone cute for you."

We walked by five times, and of course, they noticed. That table was filled with handsome men as if there was a *GQ* models convention at Ysabel that night. In less than an hour, as promised, he texted me and then came to find us. Chris picked a very cute friend for Chloe, and at that moment, I knew I would fall so hard for this guy.

At the house party, we talked all night. We were so similar. We liked the same things. We wanted the same things in life. Plus, he was so sexy. I was ready to go to his place that same night and ride him until morning. But he was very respectful, falsely assuming I was a decent woman.

"It was so great to see you again," he said outside my apartment building after giving me a ride home. "I hope we can see each other again very soon. Maybe dinner, or if you need a hiking buddy or anything, I'm down."

"I'll think about it, Chris," I teased him with a smile, "good night." It took twenty minutes for him to text me after that. I was back in the game and, for the first time in forever, I was happy not to have Richard anywhere near my life.

The day after I met Chris, he took me out on a date. We went for lunch to Ivy, and before I even noticed, I was already in his bed. In my experience, good-looking guys are not too good in bed. Well, in Chris's case, it was all the opposite. He was as hot in the bedroom as he was outside of it. I spent the night with him, and I hate to sleep in someone else's bed instead of my own, but I just couldn't get enough of him. That drive, that energy—everything about him was turning me on.

"What are you doing for Halloween?" he asked me as we lay naked in bed on a Tuesday afternoon. "Why? What are you doing?" "Actually, I'm going out of town. Thought you might want to hop on a ride." It was extremely sweet of him, and what else did I expect. He was a sweet guy. We had been seeing each other for almost a month now, but I wasn't quite ready for a holiday getaway. In fact, the idea of falling for someone terrified me. Relationships terrified me. "That's very, very thoughtful of you, but I have to pass. I've made plans with Chloe already." And I wasn't lying. We were going to this huge annual Halloween party to which I had been dying to go for a couple of years now, but every year Richard had ruined it for me. "My friend is throwing a big party. If you want, I can put you on a list." What can I say? Just the sweetest guy ever. "I'd love that very much, thanks." I scooted closer to him, lying on his chest. "What will you dress up as?" he asked, playing with my hair. "I'll be Medusa." "Medusa? Like in Greek mythology?" It was refreshing to meet someone who was educated enough to know those kinds of things. So far, everyone I told about my costume seemed to be absolutely clueless about who Medusa was. "Yes, exactly like in Greek mythology," I said excitedly. "The legend says she was a beautiful mortal woman, so beautiful even Poseidon couldn't resist, so he raped her, and when she asked Athena for help, Athena got so jealous she turned her into this creature with snakes instead of her beautiful hair." "That is a sad story," he said, sighing, "and you have chosen that for Halloween? Interesting choice." Chris chuckled, teasing me. "Don't make fun of me!" I said, pinching his shoulder. "How could I?!" He started kissing me, and all was forgotten.

Later that week, he left for New York, and I started getting ready for Halloween. If you have ever been to LA, you know that people celebrate Halloween here during the whole month of October. It's some kind of weird carnival thingy, actually quite similar to the famous Mardi Gras in New Orleans, except everyone's practically naked. Another crazy thing about Halloween in LA—you can party around town in your underwear, and it is considered a perfectly normal costume.

"I've talked to the promoter. We are on the list for the Halloween party," I said to Chloe as we FaceTimed each other to check out and approve our costumes. "Is Mia coming?" she asked, parading in front of her phone in a little French maid's uniform. "I invited her, but she wouldn't come. Not her kind of crowd." "She doesn't go anywhere with us anymore," Chloe complained to me, and I felt exactly the same way. "We could go to one of her yoga thingies," I suggested. We hadn't seen that much of her in the past couple of months since she'd stopped drinking and partying, and that made me think. "Do you think our friendship revolves around partying?" I said, sharing my worries out loud. "No! It doesn't. We love to party, yes, but there is so much more to it than that." "You're right. We should try to do the yoga class with her, though. Show that we are still her friends, and we are there for her." "We will," Chloe promised.

The Halloween week had arrived. Chloe and I had four different costumes for four different parties. We were so excited it was getting ridiculous.

The first party was on Thursday. We got on the list, thanks to Chris. Surprisingly, nothing crazy happened that night, and around three in the morning, we left the Hollywood Hills mansion and headed home. The second one on Friday was a bit more eventful, but again nothing crazy happened. In fact, the highlight of my night came at five in the morning when I got home and went to check my mailbox. Some letters for Richard had arrived, and I decided to announce it to him at 5:30 a.m. by sending a pic. 'I'll come to pick them up in a couple of days, thank you, Sophie. Let me know if you need anything,' he texted me at 7:00 a.m. Such politeness was a sign he was ready and wanted to get me back after almost two months of ignoring me. 'I'm good, but thank you.' When I found peace, he was right there to destroy it for me again.

"Why did you text him in the first place?" Chloe and Mia both asked me at the same time as I finished the story. "I was drunk and saw his name on the mail. I thought if I didn't text him right away, I would fall asleep and forget," I explained. The three of us had finally gotten together that Saturday for a quick yoga session and juice cleanse. "I don't know if you guys should do a cleanse if you were drinking all night,"

Mia spilled, apparently concerned. "We'll be fine," I reassured her, "plus it's good for us. We have tonight's party at Skybar to go to. One more night of drinking." "It's not even Halloween yet. What are you going to do on the actual date?" "What do you mean?" Chloe said, suddenly loud and indignant. . . "No one does anything on actual Halloween." I explained to Mia. "Everyone will be detoxing after the Halloween weekend. Although I guess we could go to the parade this year." "If you go, invite me, please. I don't mind joining you," Mia said, and it came as a surprise, considering she wasn't a fan of parades. "You two can go. I'll stay home that night," Chloe exhaled lazily and then turned to me, adding, "but please don't forget we are having a movie night on Sunday." "I remember." She had invited me to a screening her office was throwing somewhere in Century City near their office building, and it seemed like a good place to make some new acquaintances. All those lawyers, PR agents, and talent agents were going to be at that screening party. "Why didn't you invite me?" Mia complained to Chloe. "Like you would go? You never go anywhere with us." And even though it was a bit harsh, it was true. "If you like, you can come, but I knew you wouldn't." The air suddenly became thick. Chloe was right. After a while, we had stopped inviting Mia anywhere with us; every time, she would find some excuse not to attend, so why even bother.

After a morning of intervention, Chloe and I went to my place to get ready for the night. The theme of the party was "Burning Man," so I decided to put all of my trust in Chloe. Not only did she love all that Burning Man stuff, but, unlike me, she actually went to Nevada for the festival. "Check it out, I got the whole thing at some vintage store on Melrose," I said, putting on my costume. "That's pretty cool. I like it," Chloe said approvingly. "What do you think of mine?" "Sexy?" I said indecisively, not knowing how else to describe her stripper outfit. "Everyone is going to be there tonight. We got to look awesome." "I don't know about awesome, but we sure look like two girls from Sunset Boulevard," I told her sarcastically.

But Chloe was right, everyone was there. I don't know what it is with that place, but all the crazy stuff that ever happened to us happened at Skybar, and weirdly enough, it all began when I met Richard there two and a half years ago.

While in a line, we met at least four people we knew and one that Chloe even used to screw. "And who are you two dressed as?" I heard a vaguely familiar voice say. I turned around and saw Kai standing in front of me with some stupid panda-looking Halloween makeup on his face. "The real question is who you are supposed to be? A panda?" Both Chloe and a guy next to Kai giggled. "It's good to see you, Fifi." He stepped toward me and kissed my cheek. "It's good to see you, too. We'll see you around." And with that fake politeness, I grabbed Chloe's hand and ran into the crowd. "I don't want to hang with him and his friends," I whispered to her as we made our little getaway. "Why? What happened?" "Nothing,"

I said shortly, but she looked at me, lifting an eyebrow and demanding an explanation. "All right, fine. I just don't want things to go the way things were. First Richard, and now we are meeting Kai. I am finally feeling like I'm moving on, and I finally have a good, nice guy in my life." "So things with Chris are going well?" Thinking about him, I flushed. "Oh my! Sophie," Chloe cried out. "Shhh!" I smiled with this weird blushing smile. "He is a good guy. We'll have to wait and see where things are going."

"You ladies are looking hot," Chloe's ex-lover Andrew interrupted, approaching with a group of friends. "But what are you supposed to be?" a cute guy next to Andrew asked me. "The invitation said 'Burning Man' party," I complained, being tired of people asking us about our costumes all night. Apparently, I, Chloe, and a group of some hippies were the only ones who followed a dress code. "You look more like a Coachella girl to me," the cute guy teased me. "I'm Matt, by the way." "Sophie, and you tease me one more time, and I'll show you what kind of girl I really am." "Oh, I can't wait," he said in a flirtatious manner. All night long, we were bumping into people we once knew or even dated. It felt like a high school reunion of a kind, but what do I know, I have never been to mine.

"Fifi!" Kai called out to me when we came to the bar. "Whenever I go anywhere, I always meet you," he said, finishing his drink. "That's weird, 'cause I literally never see you," I said, chuckling. "I'll go to the bathroom," Chloe told me, sneaking out on Kai and me. "How's your brother?" I asked him, feeling, to my surprise, genuinely concerned. "He's good," Kai said simply, and then after a short pause, added, "in fact, we were just talking about you over lunch today." Why would they talk about me? "About me?" I asked, trying to make my voice sound normal. "Yeah. He was just telling his friend about a favor you did for him with some work stuff and saying what a great person you are, his little fiance." Did I hear him right? Had he just called me Richard's finace? "Finace?" He laughed. "Yeah, that's his nickname for you." Nickname? I didn't know whether it was cute or offensive. "Whose finace?" some girl behind Kai said, jumping into our conversation. "Richard's," Kai said, turning to her. "Oh, hi." She smiled at me, and I felt like I was the only one who had no idea what was happening. "Hi," I said nicely, "I'm gonna go find Chloe. Talk to you later, OK?" I touched his shoulder in a friendly manner and ran off.

The line to the bathroom was a mile long, and Chloe was not even halfway in. "There you are," I said, making my way through angry drunk girls. "OK, you have to hear this!" I said to her in my excitement. "Why? What happened?" And when I was about to recreate the full conversation for her, I heard Kai's voice. "Babe?" I turned around and was about to open my mouth and ask what he wanted when I suddenly realized he wasn't addressing me. My mouth was still wide open, and the fact that Kai made his way to and then kissed a girl who was right behind us in the line didn't help to close it. . . Both Chloe and I just stayed there staring at each other, and I knew exactly what she was thinking. In fact, I was thinking the same thing. Thank God Kai interrupted, and I didn't get a chance to tell Chloe anything in front of his girlfriend. After he was done kissing her, he turned his attention to me. "Behave, Sophie," he said, walking into the men's bathroom. Sophie. That was an interesting turn of events. I think it was actually the first time he used my name instead of "Fifi." I only smiled, deciding it was best to remain silent. "How long have you you've been dating?" I overheard someone asking Kai's new girl. "We just started dating like a couple of weeks ago, but we've known each other for almost a year." I tried to look at her and get a quick sneak peek. She was the complete opposite of me looks-wise: blond, short, chubby. What did he even like in her?

"Did you see that??" Chloe whispered to me when we finally made it inside the restroom. "I know!" I whispered back, trying to make sure no one besides Chloe would hear me. "She is so unattractive. Why would he date her?" I said in my frustration. "I don't know. She is so not his type. He likes brunettes." And that was true, or at least he had told me it was. For the rest of the night, the two of us were uneasy, spying on Kai and his girl and in the process meeting some of Kai's cute friends.

I got home that night thinking about two things I learned at the party: first, Richard had a weird nickname for me; and second, Kai liked blondes.

The rest of the Halloween week was pretty boring. On Sunday, I went to Chloe's office party, where, despite my high expectations, I didn't meet anyone except some pigs-in-a-blanket lovers and family men. And on actual Halloween, Mia and I went to the parade and were home around midnight. So that was it. Months of planning my outfits and a couple of uneventful parties were all I got for my efforts. But right when I thought everything was over, at eleven at night on Wednesday, there was an unexpected turn of events, 'Hi. What you up to?' Kai texted me out of nowhere, and to my own surprise, I did something I never thought I would. I rejected his invitation to come over. Maybe I was ready to move on after all. At least I was on to a good start!

XXVI

WICKED GAMES

"I thought of who was the last person I saw before leaving and realized it was you," Chris said to me as we were in his kitchen cooking dinner together. "I hate to be alone after a trip, and you are the best company." He was back from New York, and the second the plane had landed, I had gotten a call from him.

Two days before, I had done something I never thought I would be able to do—I had told Kai I didn't want to meet with him—and now I felt so empowered. It was a great feeling. "How was your Halloween?" "It was everything I expected," I said simply, avoiding details. After all, it was unnecessary for him to find out about all of my love drama and sabotage. "How was the trip?" I asked, changing the subject. "It was good. Would have been better if you were there," he smiled. "Here try this." I moved closer and bit a piece of chicken from his fork. "It's delicious," I said, and I wasn't lying. I was lucky enough to get myself a guy who knew his way around the kitchen.

We had dinner. We had sex. We watched Netflix and had sex again. I say it was a perfect date night. The next morning Chris was going to work, and despite him asking me to stay, I chose to go home. I was never good at hanging at someone's place, especially when the owner was not around. He got me an Uber, kissed me goodbye, and promised to call later that day. When I was less than five minutes from my place, I got a call. I got my phone out of my purse, and when I read the name on the screen, an anxiety attack suddenly hit me. "Hi, Richard." My voice was shaking, despite my best efforts to make it sound casual. "Hi, how are you?" "Good. How are you?" I asked. "Not too bad. Listen, have you received any mail for me?" "Oh, only the one I have told you about." I was referring to my 5:00 a.m. texts. "Nothing else?" "I'm not home right now. I can check the mailbox when I get there." "You are not home?" He sounded concerned. "Why? Did you spend the night with some guy?" It was unbelievable. "Even if I had, my love life is none of your business," I said, irritated. "I'll check the mail and text you. Bye, Richard." After that, I just hung up on him. The mailbox was empty, but over the course of the next few days, Richard called and texted me at least ten times. And I knew the reason. He had this magical radar. Every time Sophie seemed to be moving on and fleeing from him, the radar went on, alarming Richard that his prey was about to escape, and as the predator he was, he could never allow something like that to happen.

"Are you home today?" was the first thing Richard asked me when he called on Sunday morning. "I am for now. Why?" "I wanted to stop by to get my mail if that's OK." I wasn't very thrilled with the idea. "I'll be home till two today. You can stop by any time." "Great! Do you need anything?" he asked me with some concern in his voice. "What do you mean?" "Well, anything. If I can help you out with something, just let me know." "I'm good, really, thank you, though." I had to admit it was a nice thing of him to say.

Richard told me he was coming around noon, and for some reason unknown even to me, I took a shower, wore a nice yoga outfit, put some makeup on, and even styled my hair, which I never do. After months of not seeing the man, I had some weird excitement and joy at the thought of our reunion.

"Knock knock," I heard him call outside my door. And how could I not? For the past fifteen minutes, I had been sitting on the couch next to the door, anxiously waiting for a knock. "Hi there," I said, opening up. He was all dressed up in a white shirt, jeans, and wearing my favorite cologne, which I had gotten for him for Valentine's Day. "Hi, Sophie," he said, walking in and giving me some awkward hug. "Hi," I said one more time while he was holding me in his arms. "How have you been?" Richard asked, and before I gave an answer, added, "You look great, so I assume you have been good." I did look great. I put in a lot of effort that morning, and it was nice of him to notice and compliment me. At least I knew those two hours of struggle with my hair had not been in vain. "I'm good, actually, thank you," I said, smiling. "And you? How have you been?" "I'm not too bad. Have been better, but I'm getting there." I looked at him and suddenly noticed a lot of changes that had happened in those past couple of months. He got his first gray hair, and the dark circles under his eyes had gotten bigger, and then a scar right above his eyebrow that was never there before. It all brought me back to that nightmare of an evening. "I'm happy you are better now. I was really worried." "Thanks," he answered simply and then sat on the couch. "You have my mail?" I went into the bedroom to get it for him. "Here's all I've gotten over the past months." I handed them to him. "Thank you!" Richard said, going through the papers. "I want you to know how much I appreciate all you've done. You were such a great help, and you are a very, very nice person." "Yeah, I've heard about that," I said, chuckling. "What do you mean?" And before I took a second to even think, my mouth was already open. "Kai told me you were talking about it over lunch with your friend. So, 'little finace,' huh?" It was the first time I'd seen Richard flush red. He suddenly got so shy, unable to say anything. "Well, yeah, I was . . . you know, telling him what a good friend you are." Friend my ass. The man still had feelings, and it was clear as day. "Anyway," he rushed to change the subject, "we should do lunch sometime. I got a new house in Malibu and would love for you to come to check it out." "Yeah, I've heard about the house too." Will I ever learn to think before I speak?! "What? Who did you hear it from?" "From your brother," I said cockily, "he texted me the other night inviting to come over to the new house." He didn't comment on that and minutes later made an excuse to leave. "Thanks again for the mail. It's so great to see you, and I hope we can meet again sometime soon." "Yeah, I'd love that." He gave me another awkward hug and rushed out the door.

I sat on the couch thinking what a big mouth I had. Why on earth would I tell him about Kai? What was I thinking? And then, ten minutes after he left, Richard called. "Did you lie when you said he texted you?" he asked the moment I picked up. "I didn't lie!" I felt offended he assumed the worst in me. "I have his texts on my phone. Do you want me to show them to you?" I asked arrogantly, thinking he would say no. "Yes! I do want to see them, please." Damn! I was sure he would believe my word. "I guess he wants to fuck everyone in this town," Richard said, irritated. I knew I had done a very bad thing, and I had regretted it ten times already. It was immoral of me. "I just sent you screenshots. Don't like when people accuse me of lying!" My arrogance had gotten the best of me. "OK, thanks, Sophie." He hung up, reassuring me that he would be in touch in no time, but something told me we wouldn't see each other for a very, very long time after that little game I had started.

Evidently, Richard confronted his brother because, in less than an hour, Kai blocked me on Instagram, unfriended on Facebook, and deleted me on

Snapchat. It made me feel more like crap. Why would I open my mouth? What was my agenda? I had no idea. All I knew was that I had burned all my bridges. There was no going back, the only way was forward.

Three days after seeing Richard, he called me again, and imagine my surprise when he invited me to come over to check out his new place. I had already found the strength to say no to Kai, now was the time to muster all my courage and make that one final step to free myself from both of them. . . "We can go walk on a beach and then get back home, watch the sunset on the patio, drink something, and get dinner. How's that sound?" That sounded like a dream, a dream I was perhaps not ready to give up. "Yes, I will come over," I told Richard, without giving my decision a second thought. There was something about him that was magnetic to me. Even in the times I hated him, I still seemed to love and care for him, I still couldn't let him go. For a very long time, I had been convincing myself that what I wanted was to be rid of him, but what if, in reality, I wanted the absolute opposite thing?

"You look beautiful" was the first thing Richard said to me when he opened the front door of his new house. "You look good too," I said and stepped forward, giving him a hug. Despite my better judgment, I was happy to see him. That evening he was charming, funny, and pleasant. We did exactly what he invited me there to do, and more. In the morning, I left before breakfast, confused and not knowing where we stood or where I wanted to go from there. I was still seeing Chris, and I liked the guy very much. In fact, I was afraid that if I gave in to this thing with Richard again, he would do as he always did: make me leave a nice guy I had met and rush to him, only to ditch me a couple of months later. We had been there before many, many times, and I knew better. This time I intended for things to be different. On my way home, I texted Chris, asking to get together that evening and hang, and he was happy to do so.

Weirdest thing in the world about men. When you first meet them, they usually show themselves as these alpha-male figures. They spoil you with compliments. They enjoy taking you out. They enjoy having fun, and, most importantly, they seem to never get enough of you in bed. But as time goes by, so do the compliments, and your nightlife. All the fun seems to disappear, and instead of sex, you now have to be content with cuddles, Netflix, and snacks in bed. I have changed boyfriends over the years, but boyfriends have never changed. The same thing was happening with Chris. In just a couple of months, we went from having hot sex literally everywhere to staying on the couch all evening and eating takeout. "This is so nice," he said as we were having one of these evenings again, and to me, it was anything but nice. What was the point of hanging with him? For all those old-couple activities, I already had Richard in my life. "I'm so stressed lately, and it's great we can just hang without having sex. I'm not sure I can even enjoy having sex right now. There is so much tension and so many problems going on at work. I just want to hang with you." Those words sounded like an actual nightmare. I liked him, but I wasn't sure I liked him enough to give up my sexual life. "Sex is a very good relaxant," I said in a joking manner. "Cuddles is an even better relaxant." He pulled me closer and started hugging. I knew then and there I had gotten myself into something I wouldn't be able to handle. Without sex, there was not much of a relationship. Our connection was mostly physical, and now with that gone, I didn't see anything to keep me interested in hanging with him.

I hadn't been that confused in years, not knowing what I wanted or who I wanted, so I decided to step back and get a break from men. This also gave Richard a chance to decide for himself the direction he wanted us to move. And after a week of silence from his end, it became pretty much clear where we stood. It was almost time for my birthday, but that year it didn't feel like a cause for celebration. In fact, all I wanted was to be left alone. I told all of my friends that I didn't want to celebrate and made a plan for a short solo trip to El Matador beach, but when the date came, my girlfriends practically dragged me to a restaurant.

"You are enjoying it. Admit it!" Mia said when we were two bottles of champagne in. "I am," I said with a big, happy smile, "thank you." I looked around me at my three closest friends, Chloe, Mia, and Iris. "All of you! You really made this day special for me."

"We tried," Chloe said, refilling my glass. "We wanted to invite one more person but weren't sure if we should," Iris said, looking at me very carefully. "No, that's actually perfect, but who else did you want to invite?" My curiosity took over. "Richard," Chloe said, rolling her eyes. The feud between them wasn't a new story, but it seemed to never get old. "It's a good thing you didn't!" I reassured my girls, and I meant it. In fact, I was so disappointed with him. You'd think after almost three years, the least you could expect was a phone call on a birthday and maybe a bouquet. I didn't get either, not even a text. "He didn't even congratulate me, so he is officially the last person to invite," I said bitterly. "What about Chris?" Chloe asked. "He called me in the morning." "It's settled then. He is the guy for you." She sounded overjoyed. "And he got you flowers," Iris added. They were right, he was perfect for me, at least on paper, but deep down, I knew it was Richard whom I wanted all along. "I don't want him, I want Richard!" I admitted to them and myself. "It has always been Richard." For a moment, there was a long pause, and then Chloe sighed. "Why? Why do you want him when you have this great guy who wants to be with you?" "Why? I can't help it. It's beyond me to choose whom to love." So there it was, loud and clear—I loved Richard. I still loved him. After everything we had been through, after all the harsh words, after hundreds of breakups, I still loved him. "But I don't want to talk about him or Chris or any other men. Not tonight. Tonight, I want to celebrate my birthday with my three best friends." I raised my glass, thinking how blessed I was to call those beautiful women my friends. "To friendship!"

After dinner, Mia and Iris went home, and Chloe took me to some underground party in DTLA. As it usually goes at those places, you get offered different drugs literally every five minutes, and being convinced that since it was my birthday, there was no harm in trying something new that night, Chloe and I ended up doing Molly we got from a guy we knew. Long story short, after a long, long night of being friendly to everyone, being lovable and extremely horny, at six in the morning, I found my way to Chris's place. And then, at eight in the morning, after we had sex, I found my way out. Once the drug wore off, I didn't want to be anywhere near him. I got myself an Uber and got the hell out of that place. I was ashamed and disgusted with myself. Thinking it was all Richard's fault—if only he had called me, I wouldn't have ended up with a man I had absolutely no interest in—I got my phone out and texted Richard. 'Lol, seriously??? After almost three years of taking all kinds of shit from you, that's all I get. Nice, good to know!' Less than a second later, he got back to me. 'Ha? What are you talking about? By the way, birthday lunch today?' But it wasn't good enough, especially in the drugged state of mind I was in at the moment. 'Oh really? Call much? Never heard of congratulating someone on their birthday?' 'Why are you so aggressive? Relax' was the reply I received, and it pissed me off big time. 'I'm relaxed. Years pass, and nothing changes!' And to my surprise, instead of arguing any further, he simply texted, 'You're right, nothing changes,' and then added, 'since the plan is canceled, I say it here: Happy Birthday Sophie and I hope you become more mature this year. Congratulations.' It was a pretty good cold shower and what I needed at that moment.

After I woke up, the first thing I did was call Richard. "Do you still want to take me to birthday lunch?" He picked me up an hour later, and we went to Nobu. Not only did he get me a huge bouquet but also a present, the Chanel bag I once told him I wanted. It wasn't the expense of the gift that mattered but the fact he remembered. It made me look at him differently. A man who I thought never listened to what I was saying to him not only listened but also had a pretty good memory. The next week he took me to Hawaii as my second birthday present, and it was then I truly believed with all my heart, after all the struggles, that things would finally be different, that we would finally find the happiness both of us had so long searched for!

XXVII

NEW YEAR SAME US

They say all our troubles in adult life come straight from childhood, it all is caused by some trauma or experience we had when we were kids. It's common knowledge that women who struggle in their relationships most likely have father issues, people who can't commit probably are the children of divorce, and men who abuse women are doing so to punish their mothers for not being there when they needed them as kids. Yes, all our problems come from childhood, all the mistakes of our parents travel to our adult lives to hunt us here, and no matter how much we try to overcome these issues, there are some that can never be resolved.

"I thought for Christmas we could go to my place. What do you think?" I asked Richard on a cold December morning as we were lying in his bed minutes after waking up. "My family is going to be in town this year. Why don't we go spend Christmas with them?" It was a stupid question, considering all my history with his family, or at least with one of its members. "You know why!" I said in irritation. "I do." I knew he wanted to add some bitter comment. "Anyway, I've got you the best present ever!" I announced excitedly. I was always known as the best gift-giver, but that Christmas, I outdid myself. "I must warn you, it's a very thoughtful gift, so I'm expecting nothing less from you." "Great," he said sarcastically, "you know how much I hate this whole gift thing," I admit I did know. Not only did he hate to buy gifts, but he also didn't enjoy receiving them, or so he claimed. "Now I have to spend time thinking and worrying about a present for you. I thought of taking you shopping so you could buy whatever crap you want." "No! That won't do! I want a thoughtful, meaningful gift, and it doesn't mean that it has to be expensive." He gasped. "Fine, meaningful gift it is."

As Christmas Day was getting closer, I was getting more and more excited. For our Christmas Eve dinner, I created a menu of seven courses and a delicious pecan pie for dessert. I would do roast beef, mashed potatoes, grilled veggies, all the Christmas-table finest, and then the next morning, we would open up gifts and go to Santa's House, drink cocoa, laugh, maybe watch a movie, and have the best time.

The twenty-fourth of December had arrived, and to my surprise, everything went pretty smoothly and according to the plan. We had dinner, he complimented my cooking and my Christmas tree, we went to bed, and the next morning after exchanging gifts, he took me to the Grove, we watched a movie, walked around, finished Christmas Day by going to Nobu Malibu, and ended up at his new house. Oh, and by the way, he outdid himself with a present; not only was it romantic but very meaningful, perhaps even too personal to disclose.

"What are you doing for New Year's?" Richard asked me three days before it. "I thought we were going to be together," I said, a bit confused. "I got invited to some big Hollywood Mansion party, as I've told you." "Yes, I remember now, but I'm going to Arizona and then Canada." "Why are you telling me this three days before New Year's?" I asked, irritated. It was his typical behavior, and here I thought we were finally past that. Stupid me. "I'm leaving in two days, so we still have time to hang." It seemed not to bother him even a bit. "I don't want to 'hang.'" "Why are you getting mad? I'm telling you in advance." "Two days? You think that's the definition of 'in advance'?" Not only was it that he was leaving me on New Year's that offended me but even more so the fact that he didn't even invite me to come with him, and why was he going to freaking Arizona? "I'm taking my mom to see her family in Arizona and then going to Canada for work," he explained, reading my mind. "Fine! I hope it's the truth, though," I said, still being a little irritated, adding, "for your own sake." That was the last day of that year we spent together. He took me for lunch to Beverly Hills and dropped me off at my place. "I'll see you next year," he said when we were saying goodbyes. "Please don't kiss anyone at midnight," Richard added, smiling, "I will FaceTime you, and it will feel as if we are together." "OK, guess a FaceTime will have to do." I kissed him, wished him a safe flight, and went home to try on one more time that gorgeous ball gown I had gotten a week ago for the New Year's Eve party.

As was promised, at midnight, I got a Face-Time call. Because of the time difference, it was already 1:00 a.m. in Arizona, and he waited to give me a call and wish me a happy New Year. "You are so sweet," I said to him. "Happy New Year. I wish you were here with me," I said, and even though he didn't say it back, I blamed it on a poor connection, assuming he wished to be by my side just as much as I did. But even if Richard didn't want to be with me that night, I knew someone who did; Chris was texting me all evening, practically begging to get together. At first, I agreed to go meet him after I was done with that house party, and then right before midnight, I realized what a long way I had come. Instead of celebrating New Year's by getting drunk with a bunch of friends and going to have wild sex, all I wanted to do was to get home, wash off my makeup, and go to bed.

I would stand up Chris by ignoring his texts and then call Richard when I was in my PJ's at 1:15 a.m. By 2:00 a.m. I would be asleep. The next day I texted Chris, making an excuse for blowing him off, but evidently, he was too upset with me to even answer. Surprisingly enough, it didn't bother me even a bit.

"Everyone is going to Tulum," I said over dinner, putting my phone away after staring at IG pics of everyone on vacation in Mexico. "Who's 'everyone'?" Richard asked jokingly. "Friends, ex-boyfriends, even foes. It seems it's going to be just you and me in this town for the next week or so." "Actually, I might have to go to SF tomorrow." "What?" I couldn't hide my frustration even if I wanted to. "You just got back two days ago!" "I know, but . . ." I didn't let him finish. "Not to mention the fact that you left me alone on New Year's, and now you are leaving again!" "I know. I'm sorry, but it's for work, not leisure." He started to explain, but I wasn't done complaining. "Since you are leaving me again, I want a vacation when you are back! Nothing major. Santa Barbara will do." "Fine," he said shortly and got back to his laptop. "And why are you going to San Francisco?" "I told you, for work. There is a conference I have to attend. I'm flying in tomorrow and will be back on Wednesday." "Four days?" I asked, surprised. "What kind of conference takes four days? And why are you flying? You hate flying. You always drive to San Francisco." "I'm flying because it's faster that way. I don't want to spend seven hours driving." I wanted to disagree and ask some other questions, but he led me away, changing the topic. "Maybe we should go to Miami instead of Santa Barbara?" It was an exciting proposition on which I couldn't have passed.

We finished dinner, watched a rom-com I picked, and around 11:30, were lying in bed. "I have a 9:00 a.m. flight. I'll set the alarm for 6:00 a.m. I need to pack tomorrow," Richard seemed to think out loud. "OK, just don't wake me up," I said lazily, pulling up the sheets and covering myself from head to toe. "No, you'll sleep, and if you want, you can hang here until I'm back. I'll leave a key for you," Richard reassured me.

Despite his promise, when the next morning at 6:00 a.m. the alarm went off, I woke up together with him. "Go back to sleep," he whispered to me, noticing I was awake, and then leaned over for a kiss. He got up and started packing, and I went back to sleep. Then around 7:00 a.m., he leaned in again and kissed me one more time and whispered, "I've gotta go. Love you." After that, he ordered an Uber, got his bag, and left. I was sleepy and yet unable to sleep. I reached for the remote, turning CNN on, hoping the news would bore me to the point I'd fall asleep again. I was mistaken. Thirty minutes in and I was still awake, and then all of a sudden, my phone started ringing. The screen read Richard. "Hello?" My voice sounded sleepy. "Sophie, I need you to do something. I forgot my passport, and if I go back home, I will miss my flight. Could you do me this huge favor? Could you bring it to me at the airport?" "Yeah, where is it?" My brain was working very slowly. "Go to the closet. It will be in the top drawer on the right." It took me less than a minute to find it. "I got it," I said, putting my sneakers on. "OK, I'm getting you an Uber right now. Thank you, you are a lifesaver." "You're welcome," I said, trying to find a T-shirt. In less than five minutes, an Uber was outside, and Richard FaceTimed me.

"Can you show me the passport? I just want to make sure you got the right one." The right one? How many passports did he have? I showed it to him when I was getting in the car. "Yes, that's the one! Thank you so much. I love you!" "Love you too." The car was taking me to terminal seven of LAX. When the Uber pulled over, I saw Richard standing there, waiting anxiously. "Here's your passport," I said, handing it to him. He hugged me. "Thank you!" Then we kissed goodbye. "The car will take you home." "Oh, OK. Thanks." It was very thoughtful of him. "Have a safe flight. Call me when you get there." I kissed him again. "I will." After that, he left to catch his flight, and I left to catch my sleep.

When I got home, it finally hit me. Why did Richard need his passport for a domestic flight? Was it possible he was lying? It sure wouldn't be the first time. Or should I have more faith in him? My gut was telling me to go online and check the flight from LAX to San Francisco, but my head told me to have a little more trust, at least for the time being. The flying time from Los Angeles to SF is approximately forty-five minutes to an hour. I would give Richard up to three hours to check in. If he was really in SF, then I would know that I have paranoia, but if he wasn't, well, let's just say I would make sure he wished he were.

Four hours later, and still no phone call or text. I knew it was time to let my inner Sherlock out. The first thing I did was to check the flight from LAX terminal seven to SF at 9:00 a.m. and guess what, there was no such flight. It turns out my gut was right after all, so I decided to listen to it one more time. I changed destination from SF to Cancun and voilà, 9:00 a.m. direct flight. Was it possible it was just a co-incidence? Who am I kidding? There is no such thing as coincidence! I knew he was in Mexico, but just to be sure, I googled one more thing, and it turned out that conference he was so eager to get to wasn't even scheduled until spring. Lying, cheating bastard. If I ever thought people could change, that delusion died then and there. I'd chosen my tactics. I wouldn't say a word to him and just wait to see how long he'd let this charade continue.

I wouldn't let him get the best of me, so I went on with my day, sticking to my routine. I went to the gym, had lunch, called Chloe to gossip, went for my daily walk, watched a movie, had dinner, did some stretching, took a shower, and went to bed. A full day had passed by, and Richard still was MIA. I went to sleep with a heavy heart. Deep down, I knew that had to change, and I was the only one who could make the change possible. And yes, I know I have said it before a dozen times, but I really meant it then—it was time to break up with Richard once and for all. It was time to finally face the truth. I slept on it, waking up in the morning with even more confidence in the absolute necessity of my decision. And if I felt strong-ly before, after checking IG my case only got stron-ger. After apparently having one too many glasses of the best Mexican tequila, Richard had completely forgotten his cover-up story and started posting videos from the beaches of Tulum at night. Unable to control myself, I just had to reply to that story. 'San Francisco, huh?? Wow.' I wanted to stop at that, but my impulse was stronger than my restraint. 'I guess you think I'm a complete idiot. Well, have fun in Tulum, and please don't bother calling me when you are back in LA!' It was done, and it was done beautifully. I had no regrets. Quite the opposite, actually. I was very proud of myself. I busted his sorry ass, but what came next came as a surprise. 'This is not me, silly. I didn't take the video, I posted it for some reason.' The guy was a moron, and he thought I was probably an even bigger one. 'I am not that stupid, OK,' I texted him back. 'Sophie, I'M IN SF FOR THE CONFERENCE. I'LL CALL YOU WHEN IT'S FINISHED,' and then a little note, 'don't be stupid.' At that point, there was no turning back. He started it, and now I had to finish. 'Haha, right. Stupid is the opposite of what I am, I would be naive to fall for an excuse as idiotic as 'I didn't take this video.' There was only one 9:00 a.m. flight from LAX with United, and it was to Cancun. And if you were going to SF, you wouldn't need your passport. And I don't even want to think who you went there with. So as I said, don't bother, everything is pretty much self-explanatory.' After a roast like that, a normal person would admit he was an ass, apologize, and make some excuse, or at least wouldn't continue to lie any further, but who here said Richard was anything remotely close to normal. 'You checked the international flights, silly. I'll send you my ticket.' Reading this, I wanted to smash his face, but not to escalate the situation, I decided to simply leave him on "read". But apparently, now he was the one getting pissed. 'By the way, if I went to Tulum, it is nobody's business. Bye.' All I could do was laugh and be grateful it didn't bother as much as I expected. In fact, it didn't bother me at all. Don't get me wrong, I was pissed off with his lying. I, for one, always thought if one can't lie, they shouldn't. After all, lying is a form of art, and not everyone is talented at it, but in general, I didn't care if Richard went to Mexico, and who he went there with concerned me even less. That was the moment I realized how much I'd truly changed. Even a year ago, an event like that would have completely destroyed me, and look at me now, complete indifference. If it isn't progress, I don't know what is.

Unbothered by any of the latest events, I returned to my life, thinking it was finally a time to give Chris a call. "Hey, you," I said when he picked up. "What do you want, Sophie?" "Are you still mad at me?" "Why does it matter?" He was cold and distant, so different from his usual self. "It matters to me!" "What do you want to know, Sophie? You flake on me three times, so I got the message." "I didn't give any message!" I protested, "I simply fell asleep on New Year's. That's it." I sounded very sorry and very convincing. "Anyway, it's all good now. I'm sure you can find other dicks in town." It was true, but I didn't have time to look for them. "Who says I want others?" "What do you want from me, Sophie?" "Look, you don't have to be rude to me, OK?" "I didn't know I was rude," he said cockily. "I'm still answering your calls for some reason, so tell me, what do you want?" "I want to see you sometime, and I want everything to be the way it was." "OK," he said tersely, but I didn't know exactly what that OK meant. "OK?" I asked carefully. "OK, we can hang sometime." "I'd love that." Chris invited me to dinner at his place the following Wednesday, and it was very promising. I needed a nice, decent guy in my life, someone who would be a good influence, and he was perfect for the job.

After almost a week in Tulum, Richard was finally back. The reason I knew was the bouquet of flowers that appeared at my door on Sunday morning with a short note that only read 'I'm sorry, R.' On Sunday afternoon, after I ignored his gesture, he decided to text me. 'Did you like the flowers?' I chose to ignore that too. The next day Richard called and texted, and I still ignored him. Then he texted, 'This is my last text, Sophie!' I ignored that, too, hoping he would finally leave me alone. But anyone who knows Richard should know 'leaving alone' is not his style. 'You don't even know what's going on,' said the text I got from him on Monday. 'And honestly, I'm not sure why you are mad. I can show you my ticket, I went to SF, and then Tulum. Why should you get upset??' 'OK, Richard, as you said, 'it's nobody's business' so let's just leave at that,' I texted, but he was not going to leave it at that. 'What are you talking about?' Richard texted next, 'Let's talk it out. You are not a kid!' Whenever he was out of arguments, he would always call me a kid. Classy. I didn't answer to that, and on Tuesday, he continued his hunting game. 'Wanna watch a movie and talk?' 'No, I don't. I'm not coming over!' I was straightforward. 'Wow. I told you the truth, and you are still saying this. That's why I didn't want to tell you, 'cause you react.' 'Sure, sure, you did absolutely nothing wrong, and I'm a crazy overreacting person here lol.' I was on the edge of telling him to bugger off. 'I didn't say that. But I told you the truth, and you keep dragging this out. Let's meet and talk instead of this back and forth.' 'I'm not coming to your place, I told you! You want to meet and talk? fine, we can go to a coffee place.' 'OK, tomorrow?' I agreed to meet him on Wednesday evening, but I wasn't going to keep my word. That toxicity, unhealthy behavior, and obsession were exactly what I didn't need or want in my life anymore. I was more confident than ever that this time I would get rid of Richard and start a new, healthy, drama-free relationship with a nice guy, the one I was having dinner with the next day.

We were meeting at Chris's at 7:00 p.m., so I left my place at 6:30, feeling both hopeful and excited. Chris cooked me a three-course dinner, lit the fireplace, turned on some nice music, set the table, opened up a great bottle of French red wine—it was just perfect. He was perfect. But that perfection wasn't going to last. Unfortunately, it was doomed from the beginning. 'Hi. What time can you meet?' Richard texted me at 8:30 p.m. After I didn't answer his text for more than five minutes, he texted again. 'Hello?' and then in two minutes again, 'Where are you?' and again, 'Hello!!!' At that point, I had no other choice but to answer. 'I'm at a friend's house having dinner.' 'Can we meet after?' he asked. 'It's going to be late,' I texted him, trying to make an excuse to avoid meeting, and he obviously felt it. 'You know what, Sophie, I really tried, but I cannot take this. Enjoy! I won't bother you anymore,' but of course, he had no intention of not bothering me anymore. 'Just stay at whoever's house. Enjoy! Bye!' That's what he texted me ten minutes after his last message.

"I'm so sorry I'm on my phone all the time," I said to Chris, taking another sip of the wine. I needed alcohol, lots of it, if I wanted to survive that night. "Is everything OK?" he asked me, concerned. "Everything is perfect!" I said, smiling at him. "Thank you for dinner and for the great evening." "You are welcome." And just when I thought Richard was finally done with me and I was on safe ground, he started calling. I canceled his first call, second, and third. "Gosh, I'm so sorry!" I said to Chris, getting up from the table, "I have to take this, otherwise he will continue to call. Sorry." I walked out of the room, going to the bedroom and closing the door after myself. "What do you want, Richard?" I said quietly, almost whispering. "Where are you?" he asked me in a dominant manner. "Are you on a date?" "It's none of your business! Goodbye!" I was about to hang up. "I swear on my mother's life, if you do this, I will never talk to you again! I will never even think of you again!" "Yeah, good idea! Go ahead." I hung up, put my phone on silence, and got back to the dining room. "So sorry about that," I said, walking in. "Now, where were we?" Chris took my hand and pulled me closer, placing me on his lap and kissing me. Right at that moment, I felt my back pocket vibrating. It was R texting me again! 'Just go fuck whoever you are with! I'm done with your ass!'

After that, he texted and called and then called again, threatening, begging, and asking me to leave wherever I was at the moment and go, if not to his place, then at least home. It continued until midnight. Instead of enjoying my dinner and a sexy guy sitting across the table from me, I was dealing with Richard's never-ending drama. In the end, after he finally realized there was no chance of me leaving, he texted, 'You know what, never mind. Enjoy your night!' All that made me drink the whole bottle by myself and get pretty shit-faced. I didn't want to stay at Chris's that night, especially after spending the whole evening talking to my ex in front of him. He drove my car and me home and was very tactful about the whole thing. He parked the car in the garage, we kissed good night, and after walking me to the front door, he left. The next morning, I woke up to a new text from Richard. 'Was it worth it?' 'What?' I asked, genuinely having no idea what he was referring to. 'Was a one-night stand worth it?' 'Don't ever say shit like this to me!' I texted back, getting pissed straight after waking up. 'Shit? Shit is someone who fucks brothers, who lies and cheats!' Unable to take any more of his bullshit, I texted him two words that perfectly displayed all of my feelings for Richard at the moment. It was a good old-fashioned 'Fuck off!' and a second later, I got 'Fuck off yourself!!' back. At least we were finally on the same page . . .

Sophie Martin finished the story of the past three years of her life and looked at the therapist who was sitting across from her in a teeny-tiny office in Westwood. She found this woman through her insurance and now wasn't sure she had made the best choice. "So, this is it," Sophie said, glancing at the doctor, waiting for her reaction. "You asked why I am here. This is your answer." "No, it's not," the doctor said, carefully looking at Sophie. "You told me a story, but you didn't say why you are here." Sophie, who had never done therapy before and didn't feel comfortable in that office in the first place, now was absolutely sure she made a wrong decision coming there that day. "I'm here because of my ex," she said, gazing at Dr. Peters, unsure what else the woman wanted from her. "I feel you holding something back. You know this is a safe place. Talk to me," Dr. Peters tried to convince her. "You're kidding me, right?" Sophie, who always was short-tempered, exploded. "I've talked for an hour, told you my complete life story, and you want more? Just do your thing, give me some answers." Dr. Peters looked at her and then said, "I do want to help you, Sophie, but to achieve that, we need to work together, so I'll ask again, why are you here today?" Her voice was calm and hypnotizing, and as annoyed as Sophie was, the calm manner in which the therapist talked made her cool down. "I'm here because I can't move on," she finally spilled, sharing the terrifying truth that haunts thousands of women. "I also realized something else," Sophie said quietly, as if she was too scared to admit it. "I never wanted a relationship in the first place, and perhaps my subconscious self knew it all along, otherwise I would have picked guys who were emotionally available and didn't have a fear of commitment. I picked Richard for a reason, and the reason was simple: I was scared of commitment myself, and I needed someone to blame for things not working out. I was as much of a toxic ingredient as Richard. I sabotaged every relationship in my life the moment it got serious, then I moved on to the next person and did the same unhealthy cycle over and over again until I met Richard."

She stopped for a moment and looked down at her shoes, avoiding eye contact with Dr. Peters. Then after a moment of complete silence, Sophie sighed and continued. "I wish I was a different type of person. Someone who falls in love with one man for the rest of her life, but it's not me, not who I am. And maybe I don't know how to love but only how to be loved. I always knew Richard had darkness in him, but now I realize that my own demons are wilder than his. I use men, manipulate them, hurt them, get tired, and move on. To tire me, all one has to do is to be a nice person. With Richard, everything is different. He could never bore me, and I could never get tired of him. I could be frustrated, mad, furious with him, but never tired. The secret to that formula is simple: Richard uses, manipulates, and hurts people in the same way. We are the same. Two pieces of one dark soul. But I don't want to be that person, and yet I can't stop." When she said it, Sophie had tears in her eyes. Her usual sass had worn off, and all she had inside, all the pain and agony, were on display now. "When was the last time the two of you saw each other?" Dr. Peters asked. "Two months ago," Sophie answered honestly. "And for these two months, not a day passed by without me thinking of texting or calling him," she admitted. "And how did you end things the last time you saw him?" Sophie sighed again. It was obvious she had no desire to talk about it, but Dr. Peters's words were echoing in her head. She needs to do it if she wants to move on.

"The last time I saw Richard, he said he loved me, and he wanted to try again," Sophie chuckled. "He said he couldn't live without me in his life." Saying that she hid her eyes like a shameful schoolgirl. "And what did you say to that?" "I said I wanted to move on, and it was time for us both to try." "Hmm," was all Dr. Peters said, and then she started to write something down. Sophie was one of those women who loved to control everything in life, and that "hmm" was something Sophie wasn't going to tolerate. "What's with the 'hmm'?" she asked straightforwardly. "You told me so much about Richard, but why didn't you include your last meeting?" Dr. Peters asked with the same forwardness. "I don't know. You are the doctor here, so you tell me." Sophie's sass returned. Her whole life, sarcasm and wit were her weapons, and she mastered how to use them. "I think that you don't really want to move on." Hearing that, Sophie raised her eyebrow. It was definitely a mistake to come to this woman's office. "You said you had suicidal thoughts once," Dr. Peters continued. "Have you had them again since?" At that point, Sophie regretted she ever decided to come to see a therapist in the first place. It was her friend Liam who convinced her she needed it, and now she was thinking of all the ways she would get back at him for his horrible advice. "I wasn't going to do it; it was just for a dramatic effect." "Hmm," Dr. Peters said one more time and wrote something down again. "What's with the 'hmm'?" Sophie asked impatiently. "How many sessions would I need, do you think?" "I think I'd like to see you next week," Dr. Peters said with the ghost of a smile. "Check with Ari at the front desk. She will be happy to book an appointment for next week."

The outcome of her first one-hour session wasn't very pleasing to Sophie, especially since she was convinced one visit should be more than enough to get her life back on track. She scheduled another visit for the next week and was heading to her car when she felt her phone vibrating in her back pocket. Sophie got it out and suddenly stopped in the middle of the parking lot, frozen. A huge smile appeared on her face; Sophie received a text message. Without answering, she put the phone back into her pocket. When she got to her car, Sophie looked at it again, and a smile appeared on her face one more time. The reason for that smile was Richard Corbin. Same Richard Corbin who was the cause for her visits to the therapist, and the same Richard Corbin who just texted her, 'How's life?'